The War Orphan

Rachel Anderson began writing at 17 as teenage correspondent for *The Observer* and has also worked for the BBC and as a freelance journalist.

Shortlisted for the Guardian Award in 1978 with *Moffatts Road*, Rachel Anderson is a regular speaker on Women's Hour and writes for *Good Housekeeping* on children and childcare as well as being their children's book reviewer.

*For my Sons Lawrence Bradby
and Nguyen Thanh Sang Bradby*

RACHEL ANDERSON

The War Orphan

Richard Drew Publishing
Glasgow

First published 1984
by Oxford University Press

This edition published 1987 by

Richard Drew Publishing Limited
6 Clairmont Gardens, Glasgow G3 7LW
Scotland

British Library Cataloguing in Publication Data

Anderson, Rachel
  The war orphan. — (Swallow).
I. Title II. Series
823'.914[F] PR6051.N39/

ISBN 0-86267-185-X

Set in Chinchilla by John Swain & Son, Glasgow
Printed and bound in Great Britain by
Cox & Wyman Ltd., of Reading

PART ONE

Simon

There was a small incident on the way home from school. I was stoned by four boys and I handled the situation badly. It wasn't a mugging because they didn't want to take anything of value. It wasn't an ambush either because I already knew they were after me. It wasn't revenge because I'd never seen them before.

It was a straightforward case, I could see afterwards, of bullying. Four larger boys came for a smaller one who was on his own.

I took the short-cut which runs down a narrow path between two fruit orchards. There are hedges on each side, tall enough to protect the trees from wind, thick to prevent trespassers from stealing fruit. The sun seldom reaches down between the hedges. It's always gloomy and damp, and the weeds under the hedges grow yellow and straggly as they struggle up towards the light.

I don't like walking there, but it's ten minutes quicker than if I go round by the ring-road.

The four youths were behind, jostling and shoving each other against the spiky hawthorn as they walked. They had shaven heads, high laced DM's, black blazers and mean, narrow eyes. They were from Rosehill School. They were heading back to Rosehill Estate.

When the first stone spun past my ear I didn't turn, though I did put on a bit of speed. The second stone hit me on the back of the neck and they were closer than I'd realized. At that point, there were three things I could do. I could run like hell, or I could take no notice, or I could stop and confront them. I favoured the last. I was good at diplomacy. I gave a talk on it at the dinner hour debating club: 'Britain's diplomatic role in east-west communication'. Four people came, and two more jeered through the window, but Mr Fowler came in for the last bit of my talk and said it was well prepared.

Besides, if I ran like hell, I'd be admitting to myself that I was afraid. Fear shows. They'd know. Even if I managed to evade them this time, they'd be waiting another day. And another day, it might be worse.

But when I looked back for the confrontation, they had gone. The long path was empty.

Then, I heard stifled giggles and running feet from inside the orchard. They must have pushed through the dense hedge. Suddenly they were way ahead, darting through a gap in the hawthorn.

I looked behind. There was nobody. Even a first-year would have been a help. Bullies don't attack when there's a witness. Or a teacher. But teachers don't walk along public rights-of-way. They go home in battered cars, or on new ten-speed racers. Or a dear little old lady coming home from the shops. But dear little old ladies don't walk down this path. In case they're mugged.

A hail of sharp flints flew down from a tree overhead, and I knew I'd made the wrong decision. It was too late for confrontation or escape. I just had to keep walking along the damp path towards where they were lurking. Knowing that I should have negotiated. I should have apologized to them for being me. But you can't apologize to half-seen faces flitting behind the green leaves.

I reached the end of the path without making contact. I was out on to the cul-de-sac which leads down to the estate. I was safe, surrounded by humanity, living people behind windows, who could see me.

That's exactly when they pounced, from behind a fuchsia bush. And they dragged me down to the pavement. They got off my glasses. I grovelled in the dirt for my £37 of lenses and frames (even with the N.H.S. discount) but two grabbed me from behind and pulled down the sleeves of my blazer, imprisoning my arms. Maybe it *was* a mugging? They did want something. The third threw my school-bag over a bush into a garden, while the fourth took a knife, and touched my breast pocket with the shining tip. Quick as a flash, he slit through the stitching of the yellow, embroidered crest, and ripped through the school badge so that it hung tattered like a scab. Curiously, one of them picked up my glasses from the gutter and handed them back to me. Then they were off, they were gone.

I was ashamed to find myself trembling for the rest of the walk home. Humiliated. I had mismanaged it. I should have apologized right at the beginning.

Listen boys, I know it's not your fault you're who you are and I'm me. You want my school badge? Certainly, please have it.

Logically, rationally, I knew that I was their superior. And if I knew it, they knew it too. That was why they wanted to attack. They recognized my grey, wool blazer. It wasn't their fault. It's nobody's fault that they must live on the council estate and go to Rosehill, any more than it's my fault that my parents are well-educated, well-paid, and want me to be the same. No doubt, those boys were just as intelligent as me, but with all the wrong motivations for life. So, it was nobody's fault. Even so, I couldn't blame anybody but myself for making the first wrong decision.

'Hello darling. Good day?'

In the kitchen I stopped shaking and everything slipped back to normal. It always does. The security of the calm and perfect routine.

I kissed my mother's cheek. She kissed mine. I didn't mention the little event. She still had her dark-blue coat on and was lighting the gas for the kettle. There was no point. I'd merely ask for an extra £1.25 on Monday, as well as my dinner money, and she'd give it to me. I'd go along to the school secretary's office and buy a new blazer crest. No trouble. No questions. My mother loves and trusts me. I don't have to go around explaining things.

'Simon dear. Your ear. It's bleeding. Profusely.'

'Oh.' I dabbed at it with the back of my hand. It was. 'Only a little. I'll wash it when I go up.'

She didn't ask why I was bleeding. We've always had a good understanding.

'There's something rather vital, darling. Tony and I want to talk to you about.'

I spread two thick slices with butter and raspberry jam.

'Oh yes? What?'

Ill at ease with louts and pebbles, perfectly at ease with parents. A concert in the town hall? Dry ski lessons? Birthday present suggestions? A family party for their wedding anniversary?

Patti shuffled uneasily as she moved the tea leaves round in the pot. Then she smiled her faraway madonna smile.

'Spaghetti Siciliano for supper. About seven. That all right?'

Thank goodness. Just food again.

'Oh yep, fine.'

'Lot of homework?'

'Nope. Just about right. Eng. Maths. Lat.'

She always asked about homework, always the same question, another reassuring part of the pattern.

'We'll talk over supper then. When Tony's home.' Madonna

3

had gone. Back to the schoolteacher, she settled herself resolutely at the kitchen table to mark exercise books. At 5.30 precisely she would stop and begin to prepare supper. At 6.30 my father would return.

I took my mug of tea and my raspberry jam slices up to my room. I slotted a Vivaldi cassette into the player, headcans on. Left hand held the warm mug, right hand held the Parker 45, rolled-gold nib, size *Fine*. It always pays to get the best. Set my books carefully on the desk in the order in which I would tackle Eng. Maths. Lat.

This was the moment of perfection, the moment of beginning. There was a daft essay the other week. 'Should compulsory homework be abolished?' For goodness sake why? It's the best part. Total control over yourself and your work. It's when you really learn something.

'It's about your little brother,' said Tony.

'What?' I choked on the Siciliano.

I'm an only child.

I looked across the table at them both. My mother looked uneasy, a coy little blush, as she smiled across at my father. I looked away, down at my plate of worms, embarrassed. Were they trying to tell me she was pregnant? Funny way of doing it. We've always had a trusting relationship, open and honest.

They didn't know it'd be a brother, I thought, twisting coiling veins on to my fork. She didn't even look large. Unless she'd already had that test? On the amniotic fluid? You can tell the sex of the baby and if there's anything wrong with it, like it's going to be born a flid, or a dum-dum. They showed us a film at school. I kept on coiling. I wouldn't look at either of them.

'You might have told me before,' I muttered. I was betrayed.

'But even *we* didn't know till today!' said Tony, smiling, confident. 'They phoned your mother at school.'

'Oh,' I said. Sprinkled grated Parmesan cheese like dandruff to hide the worms.

'Patti said she couldn't say a thing, till she'd talked it over with both of us here. After all, it really *is* a family matter. He concerns us all.'

He. Why did he keep saying *he*? 'Why d'you call it a *he*? You don't know,' I said. 'Unless,' I stumbled more quietly, 'unless you've had the test?' I felt embarrassed saying it. They didn't hear.

4

'But we've always called him that, haven't we? Before we ever knew about this particular child. I suppose we always just assumed it would be a *he*.'

'There's always so many more little boys available,' Patti went on. 'It's odd, isn't it? Not that more get born. I imagine people think that looking after a little girl will be easier. I can't think why. So anyhow, the boys get left.'

I ate my spaghetti, a weight, a ten-kilo burden lifted, like in the telly ads, off my shoulders. The little boy. It was the child.

'They rang to say they could offer him to us now. He's ready. We can go and get him right away.'

They prattled on. I hardly bothered to listen. It was such a relief.

'You see, they want him to come as soon as possible.'

'Next week,' Tony added.

I'd got it all wrong. Patti wasn't pregnant.

Two mistakes in one day. A glowing blush rose up from somewhere above my knees and below my waist to fill my face with hot confusion. I talked fast to cover my tracks.

'Oh I see. How interesting.'

But they scarcely seemed to notice that I'd got the wrong end of the stick.

'How very exciting for us. But it's a bit sudden, isn't it?'

Our serene family enlarged at such short notice.

'They think he ought to move now,' said Tony. 'He's a happy little chap, but he's not had much attention. He needs to settle.'

'Into a stable environment,' Patti added.

They were like a recitation, a duet, both trying to talk at once, falling over each other's words to tell me.

'The Home he's been in is changing. There's a new housemother taking over. They feel it'd be better if he moved away before the change.'

'You see, he's been living in institutions of one sort or another all his life,' said Tony.

'At least as far as one can gather,' added Patti. She was pink with joy, her eyes were moist and bright. 'I am glad, Simon, that you think it's exciting too. I mean, *we* do, but if you do too, it's even better. And you don't *mind*?' She stretched across the table and took my hand, squeezing it gently. 'Darling Simon. We really are going into this together, as a team. But as we've said all along, we wouldn't do a *thing* if you didn't want to.'

'Mind? Of course not. I'm glad. Well, I mean it'll be a very

5

interesting experiment.'

Tony became serious, leaning forward on his elbow, adjusting his glasses. 'It won't in any way be an experiment, Simon. It'll be for always. That's why it is so important that we're all absolutely certain. They may say there's a trial period, three months.'

'Six,' Patti corrected.

'All right, six. But once you start a thing like this, involving another human being, you can't back out. Patti'll have to give up work for a week or two while he settles in.'

'Sexist!' I said. It was meant to be a joke. Because there are two males and one female in our family (unless you count the cat, but she's been operated on) we're always making jokes about whether our actions are sexist or not. We always share loading the dishwasher and hanging out the washing, except my mother's underclothes. She hangs those out herself.

They didn't seem to see my joke.

'You mean, you'd rather it was a little girl?' said Tony. 'Like Sophie?' Sophie's my cousin. She's four.

'No, I just meant the mother giving up her job to look after a new baby, not the father. Doesn't matter.' I felt embarrassed for a second time.

'He's not exactly a baby. He's more of a little boy.'

'Though she might qualify for maternity leave!' Tony said, trying to be jolly. 'And *I* certainly wouldn't!'

In their joy and their excitement, they were so sure, so certain and so stable. I felt a great rush of love for my dear, vulnerable parents. It's not like that in the books about the growth of boys. At my age, you're meant to begin hating your parents. The diagrams show it. A rush of pre-pubertal hormones surge up out of your gonads to fill the mind with loathing of everything parents stand for.

'Don't worry, Simon, we two'll have our jobs cut out as well. The little lad'll need lots of masculine support.'

We had *crème brûlée* after the spaghetti. Not one of my favourites, though I didn't like to mention it. Tony liked it. Anyway, I was so relieved, so happy that she wasn't expecting that I hardly even noticed the floppy, soggy texture as it slid off the spoon.

Of course, they'd talked about this child before. For months, maybe even years. I'd thought it was only talk. Adults love to talk, to gossip, to scheme. It's because they have less time left than we do. They have to make their empty plans. To pretend they've time. It was like that talk about emigrating to Australia. There was a job. Tony could have done it easily, setting up a new experimental laboratory. But there wasn't a job for Patti. So we didn't go. They're fair in that way. And moving house. A lot of talk about moving out of town to a place with a garden and apple trees. And a scheme to buy a new car which didn't break down every three months. That came to nothing too.

I opened a new tin of pure chunks of rabbits' liver in a rich meaty sauce, and fed the cat. She rubbed her nose daintily against my leg.

'We'll have a special celebration,' Patti said. 'Tomorrow evening.'

Food, food, always eating.

'Think about what you'd specially like for our last meal together, just the three of us.'

Saturday, I was playing a match. I'm not really in the team but both reserves were ill. We won, three-nil.

There was a woman talking to Patti when I got in, perched on the edge of the table drinking coffee. She had long, fluffy hair across her shoulders, and tight jeans and a red sweater.

She was going on at Patti as though they were old friends but I'd never seen her before. She swung her legs back and forth as though she was a kid. But she wasn't that young. She had long, red fingernails and slippery red lips.

'Miss Spaark, this is our son, Simon,' said Patti. My mother is very old-fashioned about introducing me to her friends. 'Simon, come and meet Miss Spaark, from the D.H.S.S.' She didn't look like a council worker.

'How d'you do.' I held out my hand to her. It was muddy and sweaty. We'd had to work hard for the three goals. She didn't take my hand, just waved her coffee mug vaguely in the air at me and said, 'Hi Simon. Heard so much about you.'

I decided I didn't like her. I went up to my room and started to peel off my football strip, carefully, so as not to scatter dried flakes of mud. She must have followed me up.

She gave me a fright, standing in the doorway and looking at me, just as I was getting undressed.

'Your mother said to come up and I'd find you here.'

Patti doesn't usually tell people to wander about, specially up here.

'So this is your room is it, Simon?'

7

Since I was standing in it with half my muddy clothes heaped on the floor at my feet, it was unlikely to be anybody else's room.

'Yes.'

'Nice view.' The window overlooks the river. You can see the green tops of the trees and the river-side walk. It makes up for not having much of a garden.

'Just going to get changed,' I said. 'Have a bath. Been at a match.'

I didn't like her there, looking at me. My room is private. I'd have thought any person's room was private.

She propped the seat of her tight jeans on the edge of my desk.

'That your bed?'

She put her handbag down, spoiling the perfect symmetry of my books laid out.

'Yes.' I should have said, 'No, I hang from the ceiling like a bat.'

She fiddled with my coloured pencils in a casual way. I like to keep things tidy. They're easier to find. 'Could you leave the pencils where they are? I'm making something.'

'New, are they?' she asked.

'I'm designing a present for my parents.'

'I mean, the bunk-beds.'

'No. We've always had them.' For friends who spend the night, and my uncle once slept in one.

'Ah. I thought you might have got them specially for the little boy. You won't mind, having to share?'

'No. Why should I? He'll be sleeping in the bottom bunk. I'll stay on top.'

'Then you think the whole idea is spot on, Simon?'

'Look, I really don't see it's any of your business.'

'There, I'm afraid, you're wrong.' She smiled with her luscious raspberry lips. 'I'm not here just for fun, Simon. I have to submit a report on the family situation. Nothing personal. Just part of the routine requirement in any foster plan.'

'He's going to be adopted, not fostered.'

'Yes, eventually. But the fostering comes first. You can't adopt, just snap like that. We always have a trial period. To see if things work out.'

I disliked the implication that Patti might not be able to cope.

'My mother's a teacher. Home Economics. She's been one for fifteen years. She's pretty used to children by now.'

I picked up my football shirt and put it on again. It was damp. But I didn't like the way she was looking at my chest. I'm not very big. I haven't started to grow yet. A boy in 3M has hairs.

'You probably wonder why it's all happening so fast?' She smiled with her fat, jammy lips, as though I was six and stupid.

'Not particularly. My parents've been discussing it for ages.'

'I don't know how much they've told you so far?' She began to give me a lecture about the needs of the inmates of children's homes, about the numbers of poor dear little girlies and boys growing up without the warm love of a family.

Last year, the school charity was in aid of N.C.C.H. I heard plenty of lectures like hers before. I realized that these kids needed to go somewhere. But I wasn't quite sure why one had to come to us.

'And of course, as you know, he's not white.'

'Yep. There's plenty people at my school like that,' I said instantly. Well, there was one, a West Indian, only he called himself British. Winston Pelham, who's adopted. In the sixth. He did nine O's, won all the prizes, and got grade A's right through. He's probably going to Cambridge to read Medicine. His brother's younger, in my year, only he's white. He's quite bright too. So the child was going to be brown or black or something, like Winston Pelham.

'Won't bother me. I'm not racist, if that's what you're getting at? I've always wanted a brother.' This wasn't quite true. What I meant was that I'd always admired Winston.

'You've obviously thought about it. I'm so glad. But it's going to be no good solving one boy's problems if it disrupts another chap's life. So is there anything that worries you, *ever*?'

'No.' Except you being in here. 'Nothing at all.' Then I thought better of it. 'Well, yes, as a matter of fact there is. I have wet dreams.' It wasn't true, but boys at school talked about it. 'Uncontrollable,' I said, 'with hot flushes.'

'Good,' she said, matter-of-fact, like the doctor at the school medicals in first year. 'Keep enjoying it then, that's the main thing.'

I had another try.

'And fantasies about my mother. Sometimes I stand on the landing and peek in through the door when they're making love.'

She nodded. 'Most children begin to wonder, around your age. It's only natural.'

'And I play with myself continually in class.'

She nodded knowingly as though it was all the most ordinary behaviour in the world. She flicked her fluffy curls away from her face, picked up her handbag, and got up to go.

'Altogether, you seem a sensible young man. You'll be able to cope marvellously with the changes ahead. However, placements of older children can be tricky, unexpected things. So if there ever *are* any problems which crop up, *anything* you feel you'd rather not discuss with your parents after the child's arrival.'

'I always discuss everything with them.'

'Of course. Anyway, here's my number.' She shoved a printed card on to the corner of my desk, knocking two pencils to the floor as she did so. 'And if ever you should feel like letting it all hang out, as the expression goes, remember you can call on me with complete confidentiality. The number's there. Nice to have met you, Simon. Goodbye for now.' And she went away to inspect our lavatory and our bathroom and our drains.

I picked up her card. 'J.M. Spaark, Social Worker, Adoption Fostering Unit', with a phone number and an office address.

I dropped her card into the waste-paper bin. I couldn't imagine any possible circumstances, even if it was the last day of the universe, when I might consider taking my problems to a person like her.

'Sorry about springing the social worker on you,' said Patti. 'But they do have to make sure the children go to safe homes.'

'That's OK.' Now she'd gone, I didn't mind her at all. In fact, I felt satisfied that I'd handled her rather well. I'd kept her in her place.

All afternoon I got on with my present for Pat and Tony's wedding anniversary. I always make them something. This year, I was designing hand-stencilled wall-paper for their bedroom. They didn't know about it, and there was no way they could guess. I'd bought enough rolls of plain lining paper and I was going to hand-print them. I had to experiment with wood-block ink which wouldn't run or smudge. And I had to keep it secret.

Patti fussed about for hours in my room, with a load of new stuff she'd got in. A blue plastic potty and sheets with bunnies on them. She fiddled around making up the bunk-bed beneath mine, with a rubber sheet underneath, the bunny sheets on top. Every time she came in, I had to pretend I was doing a Design Topic for school. She brought picture-books down from the attic, and put them on a chair beside the bunks, and she tucked a soft blue rabbit into the bed.

10

She was like a little girl, playing dollies.

'I'll clear out some of the drawers, shall I?' I said. There's only space for one chest of drawers in my room. 'I don't need all six.' I'd been using the bottom drawer to hide the wallpaper experiments. But I could easily move it into a box under the bed. 'I'll put my socks and vests in together, then we can share the chest.'

'Maybe just one drawer. He won't have much.'

She slid the plastic pot under the bed.

'What's all that about? I thought you said he wasn't a baby?'

'He isn't. Just want to make sure he feels safe.'

'*I* wouldn't much want to start using a potty if *I* went to live in a new home.'

'Your grandmother keeps a pot under her bed. And *she's* no baby!'

'But he might be shy.'

'Better safe than sorry,' she said, giving the bunny sheets a final smoothing pat. Suddenly she came and flung her arms around me and gave me a big hug. 'You really are a lovely boy, Simon. Being so open, and generous about all this.'

'I'm looking forward to it,' I said, carefully leaning my free elbow to cover up my designs on the desk. 'It'll be great.' But I knew that it wasn't really going to be much to do with me. It was going to be Patti's project. Tony's too, but mostly Patti's.

11

2

'Charlie 6. This is Charlie 1.'

'Get the hell out here, will you?'

'Charlie 6, this is Charlie 1. What's that? I ain't reading you too well.'

'I said, get the doc out here. We got an elephant here.'

'How's that?'

'I say, we got an elephant here. It's Schultz. He's been greased.'

'The hell he has. You stop fooling around with me and come on in. Your time is up.'

'I'm giving you straight turkey. No Christmas dressing. He bought it and you gotta send that medivac right on.'

I heard their voices keeping yapping at each other, on and on, one distant and crackling, coming in on radio waves, the other quite nearby, only a few yards away.

It was a long wait in stifling, warm air till I heard the whirling of the rotorblades overhead. The men's voices fussed in panic about the injured man. I wondered if they had never seen a wounded man before? One man, but not dead. One making the most of it, morphine pumped into his arm. I saw the stretcher swing up through the sky into the hovering medivac, and then when it had circled away, the rest of them seemed to panic.

'Any body count?' one asked above the noise. 'Lieutenant, I said, what's the body count?'

'For Pete's sake, I dunno.'

'What d'you mean, you don't know?'

'There's women and children hiding out there.'

'They're all gooks. I didn't ask for a moral lecture. We have to give the colonel a body count. OK. He wants body count. We gonna give it to him. Right?'

'Right on, sir.'

I knew I was in danger. They were going to get me if they could. I wanted to escape, but I seemed unable to move. My legs were moving but I made no progress. Their incomprehensible chatter went on rattling around in my head. They had begun to burn houses now. I could smell burning straw.

'Charlie really zapped it to us.'

'Yeah.'

'He really slapped it on, and he's gonna get it right back between the eyes.'

I began to run down the narrow path between the trees. The green ferns on either side were tall enough to hide me. The air was warm and damp because the sun never shone down here. They were after me, chasing me down the path. This time they didn't want to mug me, or tuff me up. They wanted to kill me if they could. They had an M-60. I heard the clink-clink clank. Loading it. Then the loud metal jangle of the bolt closing.

Later, their voices seemed to recede, and draw near again, one of them still insisting on body count.

'Body count, six or seven, sir. One crawled away.'

'That sixty-seven?'

'No, I said six. Maybe seven.'

'OK. Make it sixty-eight. That was some confrontation. It sure felt like we got sixty-eight.'

'Where we headed next, sir?'

'To 711833.'

'Why?'

'For Pete's sake, how should I know? He gives us the orders. I'm only second lieutenant. I'll know after we get there. OK, sweetheart?'

'Why are we here, sir?'

'To uphold all that is right. To get rid of the gooks. To stop the flood of all that is evil, sweeping across the continent. If we don't, it'll conquer the whole of the world.'

'But sir, how are we stopping it? Every time we snake down this path, they zap us and how. So then we zap back. How's that supposed to stop anything?'

'We are here to win their hearts and minds. And if we can't do that, we eliminate them. Either way, we win.'

13

3

They went to fetch him on Sunday. I couldn't make up my mind
whether or not I wanted to go too. I'd never seen inside a
Children's Home, so in the end, I went with them. Patti was in a
state. She kept saying:

'You didn't *have* to come, Simon.'

'That's OK. I wanted to.'

We stopped on the way for a meal. It was to save Patti the
trouble of cooking at home. They've always taken me
everywhere with them so I was used to going to pubs and hotels.
Tony chose the right kind of place, with the right atmosphere,
and he went in ahead to check with the landlord that it was all
right to bring in somebody under age. We were usually sent into
what they call a lounge bar.

It wasn't very cheerful in the lounge of the Golden Lion even
though the publican switched on two lights, and an electric fire
for us. The meal was re-heated shepherd's pie with tinned
carrots. Shepherd's pie is one of the recipes Patti teaches the
first-year girls at her school and she does it really well.

It wasn't just the fault of the Golden Lion. We were all three a
bit subdued.

Pattie was preoccupied. I expect she was thinking about
meeting this kid for the first time, and wondering if she'd like
him.

She told me his name was Ha.

It seemed a pretty peculiar sort of name. 'Maybe it's his
nickname?' I said. I tried to think what Ha might be short for.
'Perhaps his family used to call him that?' I suggested.

'He doesn't have any,' said Tony. 'He's an orphan.'

'Oh,' I said. 'Poor thing,' and finished up my ginger beer.

Usually, they shared the driving. All part of the equality
campaign. But Tony drove all the way. Patti was still agitated.

'Nearly there,' said Tony. Almost as though he'd been there
before. We passed down a tunnel of heavy rhododendron
bushes. The house was dark-red brick with tall gothic windows.
You might almost have expected to see bats.

'What?' said Tony.

'I said "Bats". You know, vampire bats,' I added. 'Flying round
the chimneys. It's so spooky.' It sounded silly and childish once

14

I'd started to say it.

Patti didn't say anything. Tony said, 'Oh no, you'll find it's quite a friendly old place, really.'

It was called The Chestnuts, though there were no chestnut trees, just more rhododendron bushes. We learned about rhododendrons in a lesson on Prehistory. There were rhododendrons around at the time of the dinosaurs. With thick, leathery leaves, large, brightly-coloured blossoms and dark, coiling branches, they're well adapted to grow in warm, non-seasonal climates and on the edge of upland tropical rain-forests.

It was odd to think that England was once covered in tropical rain-forest with dinosaurs prowling around underneath the rhododendrons.

The entrance hall of The Chestnuts was silent, and the ceilings high. I half felt I'd been there before, for everything was just as I might have expected an institution to be. Just coming into the building made me feel homesick. The air smelled like a school canteen, of old boiled vegetables. The floor tiles were polished to a high glare. I moved closer to my parents.

'Dreary old place,' I said.

Patti touched my hand and gave me an encouraging smile.

Shrill children's voices echoed towards us from one of the corridors and my stomach turned with apprehension. Perhaps this was the child? But it was three girls, older than myself, who scurried by, glancing sideways, giggling among themselves. I wondered how we'd recognize our child when we saw him.

'We'd better go and find the under matron,' said Patti, leading us down a corridor as though she knew the way.

We met a woman at the end of the corridor, but she didn't seem very interested in us. She didn't even know why we were there.

'Well, perhaps we should go along to the nursery then?' suggested Patti.

'It isn't the nursery any more,' said the woman. 'We call it the playroom now. You see, the older ones objected.'

The nursery, or playroom, or whatever it was, reminded me of a playgroup I'd had to go to in a draughty church hall when I was four. There'd been dozens of dull educational toys which you had to play with, and if you didn't, a woman came and made you.

This room had similar stacks of jigsaws in dog-eared boxes, gaudy plastic building bricks in biscuit tins, and battered board-games. There were about fifteen children, of different ages, playing in the room, but some of them looked a bit peculiar. A girl

15

child was rolling about on the floor, knocking her head against a chair-leg while another child, a great boy, lumbered over and bared his teeth at me in a slow, idiot grin. I hoped he wasn't the one we'd come for, but I knew Patti and Tony would have warned me if my new brother was going to be a hulking adolescent giant.

'Perhaps you'd like to help some of the little ones with their games?' said the woman.

I thought it was a bit of a cheek when Patti and Tony had come to offer a home to an unwanted child and instead of saying thank-you, or getting on with it, she expected them to start playing with all of the children. But they didn't seem to mind. Patti sat down on a tiny child's chair beside a little girl who was trying to do an impossible jigsaw of trees in autumn leaf, and Tony perched at another low play-table where some younger children were concentrating on colouring-in, politely sharing six wax crayons between them. But the crayons were so old they were dirty brown on the outside, and embedded with bits of grit, so that they wouldn't draw smoothly. I wished I hadn't come. I could be at home listening to Vivaldi and printing the first batch of wallpaper.

One small boy was crouched on the floor, by himself, playing with toy cars and making car-engine noises. The woman patted him on the head.

'Look, pet, see who's come to visit you,' she said. The little boy looked at Patti and smiled. Most of his front teeth were missing.

'Mumma!' he said, like a talking doll turned on its back, then went on with his car game.

Because of Winston in the sixth at school, I'd been expecting a black brother. This kid looked like a Chink, though he wasn't really yellow. His cheeks were more of a rosy, pinkish colour. His eyes were slanting all right, but not small slits like Chinks in comics. They were quite big really. He had a little pointy chin, and very small hands.

The idiot boy came over and tapped my arm to attract my attention. At least I could be glad that *he* wasn't going to be my brother. I gave him one of the wax crayons, but he didn't seem to know what to do with it. Instead, he shambled purposefully off on a journey round the room, touching each of the walls with the tips of his fingers. Then he stopped in front of the fireplace. It was a big old-fashioned one with ornate, carved woodwork, and the grate had been blocked off with a square of hardboard. The mantelpiece was used as a bookshelf with a row of annuals and Ladybird books ranged tidily in order of size. He stared intently up at them, touching each methodically but not taking them down.

Suddenly an acute pain stabbed at me like a knife into my stomach and I felt the room spin round.

'What's up, Simon? You all right?' said Tony. 'Looking a bit washed-out all of a sudden.'

'Got a pain. Think I need to go to the lavatory.' I left the room quickly and Tony followed me.

'I'll take you,' he said.

He led me along to some cloakrooms. He could find his way about this place nearly as easily as Patti could. In the cloakroom, as well as children's coats, there were several folded wheelchairs against one wall and calipers and straps hanging from a hook. Tony waited for me, leaning on a radiator.

'Better now?' he said, while I washed my hands.

'Yes, thanks.'

'Must have been that shepherd's pie. Come to think of it, it did seem a bit off, didn't it?'

But I didn't think it was really the pie that made me feel ill. After all, he'd eaten it too, and it hadn't made *him* ill.

By the time we got back to the playroom, the woman was organizing Patti to take a small group of the children for an expedition into the garden.

'And perhaps you'll take Melissa too, will you? She's had nobody to visit her for weeks, and she does so enjoy a treat.'

Melissa was the one who'd been doing the 1,000-piece jigsaw but she couldn't talk.

Just getting the hulking adolescent into his anorak, and Melissa into a wheelchair, took nearly ten minutes. Patti pushed the wheelchair. The incredible hulk wanted to be with me and staggered along clutching my arm. Tony carried the little boy who was going to be ours in a piggy-back ride.

His legs were thin, like sticks, and in comparison, his feet seemed enormous. Both his shoe-laces were undone, and kept flapping about, which can't have helped his walking.

Tony jiggled the little boy up and down on his back which made him giggle, and Patti chattered away to the silent girl in the wheelchair about the fat green buds on the rhododendron bushes and how they'd soon be pretty flowers.

Patti and Tony were both trying to be very jolly but it was a horrible garden and so was the walk round it. There were straight concrete paths, and a climbing-frame with its feet embedded in more concrete. But you couldn't get in and climb on it because it was surrounded by a high, chain-link fence with a padlocked gate. I supposed it was some kind of safety regulation, like having the fireplace in the playroom closed off.

As soon as we came in from the garden the woman was waiting for us, impatiently, as though we'd spent far too long walking along the concrete paths. 'Housemother's ready to see you now,' she said, and led us to the housemother's office in another part of the house.

The housemother sat behind a desk, like a head-teacher. We were offered three chairs, the opposite side of the desk. Ha hung back in the doorway.

'It's all right, Robert dear,' said the housemother. 'You may come in with your new family.' Ha sidled in a few steps. 'I always called him Robert,' the housemother said to Patti. 'It seemed better to give him a more natural sounding name. But, of course, you will do what you feel like.'

We were brought strong, bitter tea, with two plain biscuits balanced on each saucer. The little boy wasn't offered any.

It wasn't a tea-party, more an exchange of formalities.

The housemother pushed some papers across the desk at Tony. 'That's his Home Office entry number. The medical card. He's had the usual inoculations. Polio, diphtheria, all marked there. As to the early years. Oh yes, I take it you notified your local office of your intention to foster? It *is* a legal requirement, fourteen days prior.' She droned on. It had no bearing, as far as I could see, on my life, nor on the life of the little boy lurking by the door. I caught his eye and winked, but he looked away, down to the polished floor. I made a funny face at him. He liked that. He started to smile but then stopped and turned away to stare out of the window.

'In the event of the need for anaesthesia, you'll have to return here for my signature,' said the housemother.

'Good heavens,' Patti burst out. 'I sincerely hope we don't need to start worrying about operations.'

'Accidents can happen at any time.'

'Exactly,' said Patti crossly, 'And what happens if he needs treatment in the middle of the night? Are we supposed to drive all this way just to get your signature?'

'These *are* legal requirements,' said the housemother coldly, 'established for the protection of the children. If consent for anaesthesia is required after my departure from the centre, my assistant matron is authorized to sign. Or, of course, my successor.'

The little boy wrapped himself in the long curtains and stared out into the dark garden.

'Perhaps you'd sign here? Yes, both of you. Just the usual form. It in no way interferes with your other arrangements with the worker in your own area.'

As soon as they had signed, the housemother stood up and shook hands with them across the desk.

'Goodbye,' she said without a smile. 'No doubt I shall be seeing you again in court. If all goes well.' She might have been handing over a car.

We followed the other woman to collect Ha's things. Every corridor had heavy fire-doors, at each end, with small window panels set so high up you couldn't see through.

Somebody must have been obsessed with the danger of fire.

In the dormitories the beds stood in a line down one wall, each covered by a matching cotton bedspread, without a crease. There were no toys, or books to distinguish which child slept in which bed. But the little boy slid along the shiny, polished floor and under one of the beds. Hidden beneath it was a sliver of used pink soap and half a biscuit, both of which he retrieved, and put into his pocket.

While Patti helped the woman pack his things into a holdall, the little boy suddenly grabbed my hand and pulled me to look at a wardrobe standing in the corridor. He didn't say anything, just pointed. At the bottom of the cupboard lay a dried fir-cone, a broken dinky toy, and a couple of tattered old comics, a *Commando* and a *Warlord*. The *Commando* was rolled up. The front of the *Warlord* was unrolled and showed a hawk-eyed Marine with huge, hairy forearms striding aggressively across the cover. 'Follow me, Bud!' said the speech bubble coming from his grim lips. 'Zap! Zap! Zap!' said the jagged lettering in the bushes around him.

I left the comics, and picked up the dinky toy. It looked like a truck I used to have as a kid. I picked it up, turned it over to read what it was.

'Great,' I said. 'It's an Alvis Stalwart. I used to have one the same. Pity about the wheels though.' It was broken and scratched.

I thought they were his things and he was going to bring them. But as soon as I'd looked at them he pushed them to the back of the wardrobe and closed the door.

'Aren't you bringing them with you?' I wondered why he wanted to leave them behind.

A bell clanged along a passage. My stomach-ache had gone but I felt even more depressed. It must be terrible to be bossed about all day by bells and women. And I knew we had to get this little boy out of here too. I knew I wanted to take him home with us. Yet I felt afraid of even touching him in case it upset him. I went to help carry his holdall. But as soon as he saw me near it, he grabbed it from me and gave it to the woman helper to carry.

Tony put a gentle, but restraining hand on my shoulder. 'Don't rush him, Simon,' he said quietly. 'Better let him take his own time.'

When we were in the car, the little boy slid along the back seat and on to my knee. I don't remember ever having another boy sitting on me before. He smiled up, then put his two middle fingers into his mouth, in the gap where his teeth were missing, and his head drooped down against my shoulder, and he fell asleep.

I don't think I'm very attractive. My nose is too large, and my skin pallid, and my eyes bulge behind my glasses. I could tell that this little kid, even with his missing teeth and spindly legs was very pretty.

Patti turned from the front passenger seat and took a look at Ha sleeping against me. She smiled approvingly. I had pleased her. Little Ha had pleased me. I was somebody new. I had a little kid brother, who loved me. I felt that I could probably come to love him too if I tried.

It was dark driving home, so I couldn't look out of the window. But with the boy asleep against me, the return journey seemed quite short. I just sat content with my little burden. It was so easy. So much for dear Miss Spaark, telling me how difficult it would be.

I went up to bed early since it was school next day.

I said good-night to Patti in the hall as she came down from putting him to bed.

'I do love him, Patti,' I said. 'I'm so glad he's here.'

'Yes Simon. Good-night.' She didn't seem willing to hang around in the hall and chat. She kissed me, but carefully, in the shadows, so I couldn't see her face. Her cheek was all wet.

I went to the sitting-room and kissed Tony good-night.

'Quite an emotional day all round,' he said with a smile. 'Don't forget, Simon,' he added, as I was half out of the door. 'We still love you, too.' What an odd thing to say. I had never doubted it.

'Goodnight, Ha,' I said, from the top bunk. I didn't kiss him. I've always kissed my parents and my grandmother but I didn't know whether brothers and sisters kissed one another. So instead, I leaned over the edge of the bunk-bed and patted the top of his black, glossy head in a friendly way. Good boy.

He lay still, wide awake, but not moving, like a golden-skinned, oriental dolly, clutching the blue rabbit that Patti had put for him. I could tell he was pleased to be here, sleeping in a proper bed, with us, in a real home, our home, part of a family at last.

'Bet you're glad to be here?' I said.

He fixed me with his brown eyes and stared, not exactly smiling, but almost.

'Goodnight then, Ha, I'm turning off the light now. Sleep well,' and I switched off the clip-lamp by my head.

Before I went to sleep, images from the children's home, which I hardly noticed at the time, kept swimming into my mind and wouldn't go away. I saw a faded poster of a nursery rhyme stuck to the blue wall with pieces of Sellotape and the bottom corner was torn so that Humpty-Dumpty's foot was gone. I saw the picture-hooks on the mantelpiece over the blocked-in fireplace, and they were too high to reach. I saw the reinforced glass mesh high up in the fire-doors. Perhaps they were things which Ha remembered too.

I woke in the night feeling ill. It was seasickness. The liquid surface of the earth swayed back and forth, up and down, swinging me rhythmically from side to side. I was in a small craft, buffeted this way and that.

I was nauseated, submerged in a sickness and a hopelessness which nothing could shift. Then, strangely, the fluid movement which sickened me, also lulled me back into half-sleep.

Next time I woke, the motion had stopped and the room was dark. I wanted the light on but I couldn't find it. So I lay still, my heart beating heavily, my body damp, unaccountably afraid.

From outside, like thunder, came the deep rumbling, a distant roar. It drew closer, dissolving as it approached, to an intense mechanical scream. Too alarmed to sit up, to get out and cross the room. Too frightened to call out for help, in case anybody heard me. Despite my fear, I opened my eyes in time to catch a glimpse through the window, high on the wall, of the dark shape against the night sky. It swooped towards me with a high whine, as though it would dive directly in through the window and into my head. Wide, swept-back wings, and sharp, needle-pointed nose. Red lights sparkling at its wing-tips and underbelly. It travelled so fast that the red lights melted into a scarlet streak matching the scream of noise, and it passed away overhead. Then the distant roar repeated, turning again into a mechanical scream, and another black shape passing overhead, and another. Three in all. They nearly touched the roof, and so low the window glass rattled.

Then nothing. It was all done in less than a minute. It didn't add up to anything I understood. I didn't know what they were doing up there, only that they carried fear, and radiance through the sky.

I never dream, not so that I'd remember in the morning. But I remembered instead something my Granny once told me. 'Often, it's what happens to other people,' she said, 'what you only hear about, that hurts most of all.' I hadn't understood what she meant, any more than I understood the strange noise in the night.

Our weekday breakfasts are smooth and speedy. We each do our bit quickly and automatically. Not colliding in the kitchen, not uncivil, just efficient. Seeing to the toast, the tea-making, setting out the cereals, snipping the corner off the juice carton.

We don't talk much. We listen to the news on the kitchen radio.

On Monday morning, the new little chap changed all that. He was surprisingly inept. He couldn't do much for himself — dress himself, or wash himself. He didn't get out of bed until Patti came up for him and helped him out. He was afraid of the stairs. He wouldn't come down on his own. Patti had to hold one hand, and lead him, guiding his other hand along the bannister which he clutched tightly.

At breakfast, he wouldn't feed himself, so Patti couldn't do her share of getting the table set. She had to help him. She lifted him on to a chair and set some cereal in front of him. He looked at it, unwilling to do anything with it. She sat down beside him and showed him how. She shovelled the Weetabix on to the spoon and handed it to him ready to pop into his own mouth. He picked up the spoon awkwardly. It didn't reach his mouth. Milk-sodden gobs of Weetabix slid to the floor. The cat came and sniffed under the table. Usually she likes Weetabix, but today she wouldn't touch it.

Half-way through the bowl, Ha gave up trying to feed himself, and Patti had to do it for him. He opened his rosebud mouth like a baby thrush in the nest, waiting for worms. Then Tony went and fried eggs and bacon.

'Cooked breakfast?' I said with pleasure. We usually only had fry-ups on holiday.

'Ha needs a bit of building-up. High protein diet,' said Patti.

'Oh good. Can I have some too?'

When it was time for toast, Ha couldn't cut it himself, let alone spread butter and marmalade. Patti had to do it all, until Tony said, rather sharply, 'Come along, darling. You must have your own breakfast. Your tea's getting cold,' and they changed places so that Patti could eat her cereal, while Tony patiently fed tiny toast fingers into Ha's open mouth.

'You just have to encourage him a bit more,' said Tony. 'Don't do it all for him.' Tony poured Ha a mugful of milk, and handed it to him. 'Come along, Ha, here's your drink, old chap.'

Ha looked at it. He didn't know how to pick it up. Instead he lowered his face, and tried to drink from where the mug stood, brimming, on the table. So much for Tony thinking that encouragement alone was enough.

'See, darling!' said Patti. 'I told you! We really *do* have to help him.'

'Don't shout, both of you,' I said. 'He doesn't understand. It won't help shouting.'

After being brought up in that awful place, it wouldn't help him feel he wanted to stay here with us, if they yelled at each other.

I buzzed off to school quickly. The delayed start to breakfast meant it was already ten minutes later than usual, and I had a two-mile walk.

I slid into Assembly just in time. But coming out of the hall, I got a D.T. for not wearing a badge on my blazer. I'd unpicked the slashed one, but forgotten to bring money for the replacement. Old Unwin, who handed out D.T.'s like Smarties, is a deaf stick, so I didn't bother to explain about the louts.

Nor did I explain to anybody about Ha. They wouldn't be interested. It's a large, anonymous school. The staff haven't time to distinguish one boy from another, let alone bother about what happens when they aren't in class. Not like primary where every detail of home life quickly became important Class News.

'Today, Justin O'Mara's mother had a baby, isn't that right, Justin?' and Justin would nod, and climb up on to his chair so that we could all clap his success, even though the effort had been not his, but his mother's. And then, up on to the Infants' News Board it went. 'Today Justin O'Mara has a new brother', which led Miss Golden on to talk about the class hamster and how it wouldn't be having babies because it lived alone.

How I'd envied Justin. And his glory lasted all day, for at going-home time, he was fetched not by his vast floral mother, but by an elder brother on a motor-bike.

All day in class, the remembrance of Ha at home, the private news of his existence, kept floating into my mind and I felt a lurch of exhilaration in the pit of my stomach. I wanted to tell people about him, especially Winston in the sixth who was adopted too, yet I felt that if I did, it might break the enchantment.

After school, I ran most of the way home, with Biol., Maths., and Lat., bouncing in the schoolbag against my back. I hurried down the orchard path, not from fear but impatience to be home.

Boys of my age aren't supposed to love their parents. They're meant to be sulkily dependent on mothers, resentful and competitive towards fathers. It wasn't like that with us. I cared for Patti and Tony in a calm, loyal sort of way, like they cared for me. We made a trusting trio. But this new feeling for Ha was quite different.

It was bizarre. I'd known him less than a day, unless one counted from Friday when I first heard about him. Even that only made three days. In that short time, already I felt certain that he'd get on with me. I felt a strong desire to cherish and protect him in all the many ways a young child needs. And until he'd learned self-reliance, and an ability to care for himself, this little boy needed it more than most.

He was curled up in the armchair, sucking his two fingers in the gap between his front teeth, and hugging a cushion against

24

himself like a soft toy.

'Hello, Ha.' He looked up, with a quick look that might have been a grin. I took it as approval. Hi, kid brother. Big brother's home. If I'd known to look more carefully, I might have seen that it wasn't a grin and it wasn't approval. It was terror and anger mingled.

Patti was in the kitchen. No schoolbooks to mark, she'd not been to work. She was making supper in a half-hearted sort of way. She made me a honey sandwich but I didn't go straight up to see to the Biol., Maths. and Lat. Instead I settled down with Ha to watch a bit of television. The man on *Blue Peter* was talking about billeting a homesick Sikh regiment in Brighton Pavilion during the Second World War. I wondered if Ha understood what the documentary was about. I watched him out of the corner of my eye, his pretty face turned to the screen, concentrating intently, his eyes reflecting the moving lights, absorbed in the programme, just as I used to be at that sort of age.

In some ways, I felt sure, he was going to be very like us. Not to look at of course, but in his personality as a quiet and thoughtful person. But the fact that he didn't talk made it difficult to know quite *what* he was thinking. The programme ended, and an American cartoon started.

'That was interesting, wasn't it?' I said.

He nodded enthusiastically. 'Maybe we'll be able to go to Brighton one day.' I picked up my schoolbag. 'Got to go and do my homework now, Ha.' I found I was saying it loudly, almost shouting, like Patti always shouts at my grandmother if she wants to make sure she's heard. 'Be down again soon.'

I went to fetch another sandwich from the kitchen first.

'Another?' said Patti. 'Then you won't want any supper.'

'Need the honey,' I said. 'Helps me think. Glucose is rapidly digested early in the alimentary canal before reaching the ileum, and so is quickly distributed, via the blood stream, to reach all parts of the body, including the brain, within two microseconds, and restores me to full intellectual efficiency.'

'Oh, I see. Ha OK?'

'Watching *Mighty Mouse*.'

'It's good to see how he's settling, isn't it? But I think he must be tired from the excitement. He's unusually quiet.'

It didn't seem unusual to me. As far as I could see, he'd been not just quiet, but totally silent since he arrived.

'Why doesn't he talk? It's going to be difficult communicating with a non-speaking person in our family.'

'It's frustrating, I know, darling. Miss Spaark's going to arrange something about it. Till then, we'll manage, don't worry.'

'Is it because he's Chinese?'

'He's not Chinese. He's British.'

'So why won't he talk properly?'

'He's been very traumatized.'

'What's that?'

'Made unhappy about a lot of different things.'

I didn't see why he should go on being unhappy now he was with us. I would have thought that coming to live with us was the best thing that could have happened. Perhaps he'd soon begin to realize that coming here was a good thing, and that he was quite secure.

'Most children from institutions are like that. They just don't get enough individual attention. They don't ever feel loved. So they can't flourish.'

'But he'll be all right now, won't he?'

'Yes. Better still once he starts school.'

'Tony said we weren't to rush him. He might not be ready for school.' I still remembered how terrifying I'd found it moving up from Infants to Juniors at All Saints' Primary. I must have been at least eight, and I'd still cried sometimes. 'I mean, d'you think he could cope? How old is he?'

She didn't answer, but merely asked if I wanted another cup of tea before I went up, and then went on chopping at the onion in one of the numerous Cordon Bleu methods. There are eight different ways of slicing onions, she had once told me. There's the way for *jardinière* of *légumes*, and there's skinning it whole for some kind of chicken casserole, and thin slices for a salad, and rings for deep-batter-frying. She was chopping this one into transparent fragments for her elaborate stew. The great thing about Patti is, that even when she's not out at work, she's busy practising skills and learning more.

'About seven, I suppose,' she said evasively, and tipped the fragmented onion bits into a pan of sizzling butter.

'About? That's funny.'

'We're not sure. We haven't got all his papers here. So we don't know much about him yet.' It seemed unlike my careful parents to adopt somebody they didn't know about.

'Nobody's age is "about" something,' I said. 'Until you get to Granny's age, and then people pretend to forget. Aren't people's ages stored up in a government office, somewhere in Somerset?'

'Not Somerset. Somerset House, in London, yes. But Ha's won't be there. Would you like another honey sandwich? And then you'd better get on with your homework, or it won't be done before we eat.' She began the skilled chopping technique on some mushrooms.

'It must be there. Everybody's are. You said so when Grandfather died.'

'Everybody's who was born here. But Ha wasn't born here. He was born in a war.'

She said it as though it was the most ordinary thing in the world. Born in a war. In a war. In a war in a war war in a warawarawar in a warrawar. The three words echoed round the kitchen, bouncing off the fluorescent strip lighting and spinning through my ears so that I seemed to be falling through space. I righted myself.

'I said you really *must* go and start your homework, Simon.'

'Which war? Why didn't you tell me?'

'It isn't important.' Now a pile of carrots was coming in for the savage slash and kill technique.

Not important? How could she believe that? War is extremely important. Everybody knows.

'Well anyway, you didn't ask about him.'

True. She'd got me there. I hadn't thought to ask. I'd been so busy thinking about my role as big brother that I hadn't wondered where he came from.

'Does he know? Which war?'

She told me in brief and meaningless sentences. A civil war. A complicated war, messy and long drawn-out. In a small, thin country. In South-East Asia. First against the Chinese, then the Japanese, then the French, then the Americans.

'Why?' I said.

But she didn't say. Perhaps she didn't know.

'What about us?'

'It was mostly the Americans,' she said. 'We were never really involved, except to send aid.'

Dear Ha. He had seen things I couldn't even imagine. He had really *lived* in his brief life while I had merely filled my head with maps of the alimentary canal, chemical formulae for gases, and verbal conjugations for a dead language. Everybody had their war, except me, all wars merging into one magnificent whole. There was Grandfather's war, the war to end all wars, when they

27

wore strips of khaki cloth bound round their legs, and our headmaster's war when he'd had to run for the Anderson shelter in the night wearing pyjamas, and the Trojan war, and the Wars of the Roses. Even Patti had her war. Evacuated to Devon the day she was born.

Now, through Ha, I too could be bathed in the glamour of history. If I had already felt tenderness for Ha, I now felt bound to him. He was my own war orphan. I would do all I could for him, I would serve him all my days.

'Does he know?'

'Know what?'

'About his war?'

'He was very young. He's lived at Chestnuts a long time.'

'He ought to know.'

'Maybe. In time. When he's ready. He was only a very small boy.'

Miss Spaark called, but I kept well out of her way. She didn't have to inspect my bedroom a second time. I knew she'd come to gloat, to see how badly one pre-pubescent boy was adapting to his new brother. She was going to be disappointed. Ha's arrival was the most invigorating thing that had ever happened.

As soon as I heard her grating whine in the kitchen I went out to the Public Library. The section I needed was crammed with books. The titles alone told me the beginning of the story I wanted to hear. *Eyewitness in Asia, Not with Guns Alone, The Unheard Voice, Inside Story of a Guerilla War, The Blazing Heart: five dedicated men lived, fought, and died together through seventeen months of the most bitter war of our times.*

The best book of all was *Jungle Warfare, an account of the South-East conflict, 1954—1975.* I thumbed through the pages. Here, in a single volume was everything *I* wanted to know in order to be able to help Ha to know all *he* needed to know.

It was a big glossy book, with lots of maps, diagrams, statistics and pictures about tactics, troops and weapons. There were photographs of flame-throwers in use, heavy guns with tongues of fire flickering down the long barrels, assault rifles, tanks and planes, the whole gleaming technology of modern war.

Some would need decoding. M-16, M-14, SKS and M-48, 60-mm, 130-mm, C-119, and C-53 were the expressions of another language. What was the difference between CH-47 and B-52, between LZ and DMZ? The flying capabilities of the Bell AH-1

28

Cobra were pointed out, but how did it compare with the UH-1 on the next page? What or who was ASSID, NID, CIDG and MACV?

But this was what my education had been for. The book was waiting to be deciphered, then it could speak. I would interpret, and Ha's life would be clarified. It was as straightforward as a chemical formula. The meaning was there. It was simply a matter of studying it, till the answer was revealed.

I put the other books back on the shelf and carried *Jungle Warfare* quickly over to the counter to be date-stamped before anyone else wanted to borrow it.

The woman ahead of me in the queue had six fat novels about love affairs with the pages softening at the edges from constant use. I flicked through the pages of my book while I waited. It showed a very different world from hers. I knew that some of the pictures were shocking. There were children, naked, their skin in flames, running down a road and screaming a silent scream because pictures don't talk. Children smiling, gathered round a tank tipped on its side. People eating rice from little bowls, neither smiling nor screaming, merely eating. There were wounded soldiers and houses on fire. There was a pilot dangling upside down by his parachute strings from a tall tropical tree in a rain-forest, and a man being shot in the head with a pistol, his eyes screwed up, waiting for the bang like you do with fireworks.

I wondered if I *ought* to be shocked by these images, to turn the pages quickly like one does with diagrams of people making love at peculiar angles.

But they didn't shock me. They fascinated me. It was part of history. These things must have happened. Somebody must have been there with a camera. If they happened, the rest of us ought to know. All the same, I thought I probably wouldn't show Ha the gruesome pictures till he was properly ready.

I knew it must be Ha's war because the people looked like him. High, flat cheeks, straight, black hair with a gleam on it. It was easy, looking at the pictures, to see that Ha wasn't a Chink. He was one of those people, born in a real war.

It was my turn at the counter. There were so many people waiting that the librarian was stamping books mechanically without even looking at the books or the borrowers. She date-stamped *Jungle Warfare* quickly, just as she'd stamped the six love books before it, and slammed it shut with a half-hearted grunt, and moved on to the borrower behind me. She was working so fast, that her hand holding the date-stamp knocked against *Jungle Warfare* by mistake. It fell open at a page showing five people who looked as though they had been burned alive. I read the caption upside down. 'Peasants were often the chief casualties.' The photograph showed the charred bodies, two large, three small, piled up neatly, ready for identification, but looking more like goods for sale on a market stall. The dead heads were flung back as though gasping for air. Asphixiated before burned. The dead eyes no longer elongated Asian olives, but deep holes which had been looking out at a last view of the world before surrendering to death by fire and an eternity in darkness. The bleak mouth-holes looked like dried beaks. Five dead people. From upside down, they looked more like bar-becued fowl than people. I craned my neck.

The librarian had also been captivated by this awesome picture and, for a long moment, she too stared. Then she snapped the book shut with a sharp sound like a shot which rang through the respectful atmosphere of the library. She slid the book over to her side of the counter.

'Just a moment,' she said. 'Dear,' she added.

She sorted through the box of borrower cards till she found mine. It was a different colour from the rest.

'It's a Junior card, isn't it, dear? Wait a moment please.'

She scuttled to an inner office with the book and the card, leaving the people behind waiting. They looked like O.A.P.'s. They probably had nothing better to do than stand in a line in the warm. I could see through the office door where she was talking to somebody else.

She came back smiling, without the book. She handed me back my green ticket.

'Here you are, dear. Sorry. Bit of a mistake. It was meant to be in reserve.'

'What?'

'In reserve collection.'

'Could I leave my name, and have it next?'

'No, dear. It's not reserved for anybody. It's part of a special collection.'

'I got it off the shelf, over there.'

'Yes, dear. I know you did. But there are certain categories which you aren't supposed to take out on a Junior ticket. For your own protection.' She had a loud, piercing voice. Everybody could hear that she was censoring my reading. I wanted to scream and shout at her.

'It was for somebody else at home,' I said, very quietly.

'Then they'll have to come in and collect it themselves. Provided they have an Adult Borrower's ticket. A blue one, like this.' She carefully pointed out the tray of blue cards in case I was so daft I couldn't work out for myself the difference between the blue tickets and the green.

The man behind began to push forward impatiently. The librarian took his books. He had two detective novels and a biography about Nelson.

'I'm very sorry, dear,' the librarian said to me, as she stamped the man's books. 'I'm sure you understand. Some books aren't, well, you know.' I knew. Dirty books, blue books. Anything we aren't supposed to know about. She thought I was a child. I *am* a child. But not an innocent child.

It was my height betrayed me. I'm short. Tony's short. The Picts were short. And the Scots. And the Chinese. And the Pygmies. If you're short, and a child, you get treated like some kind of infant moron.

Unstead, in my class is five foot ten. He gets into all the films. He buys cigarettes, goes into pubs, no bother. Same age as me, and half the understanding of the world. I bet Unstead would have been allowed to have *Jungle Warfare*.

I went on standing. When she saw I wasn't going to move, the librarian called one of the younger assistants.

'Our Junior Library's very good. I'm sure Janet here can help you find something more suitable.'

The woman from the Junior Library led me across the hall, almost by the hand, as though I didn't know perfectly well where the Junior Library was. I didn't want junior knowledge. Ha hadn't had a junior war, a special censored children's war. He'd had a real one.

'Which particular aspects were you interested in?' she asked.

The aspects in the book I'd already chosen.

She was young, and spotty, but quite kind. She searched out some kids' picture-books, things like *Children of Other Lands*, and *How we Live Today*, with photographs of primitive houses on stilts standing in shallow muddy rivers, Buddhist temples, and open-air market scenes with exotic brightly-coloured fruit for sale. Nothing about wars, and no barbecued hen people.

They weren't the sort of facts I was after, but they'd have to do.

'Is it for a school topic?' she asked.

'No, nothing to do with school.'

'The other book you saw. She's a bit of a bear, the Deputy Chief. But I should think you could probably read it in the Reference Library if you wanted. What was it called?'

'I've forgotten now. It doesn't matter.' Grudgingly, I took the books she'd found for me. 'They're for a little boy I know,' I said. I didn't want to look a fool, walking out of the library, carrying picture books suitable for seven-year-olds.

I was followed, all the way home, by the image of five burned bodies.

4

Ha was squatting on the floor surrounded by coloured Lego bricks. I used to play with them when I was younger, to build little cars and trucks and villages.

'Hello, Ha. I've got something here to show you.'

He looked at me strangely, staring hard, as though trying to sum me up, though I don't know why he had to sum me up just because I came into the room.

'I chose these books specially for you, from the library.' I sat on the armchair and he leaned against me, as though wanting to climb up on to my lap. He was heavy, but I let him stay, and I held the book in front so that he could see the pictures while I read the words.

> Rice, *the principal food of over half the world's population, grows well in a warm moist climate.* The Mekong River, *the tenth largest in the world, is four thousand kilometres long and flows into the South China Sea.*

'Are you listening, Ha? Because a long time ago when you were a baby you lived here, so I'm going to teach you about it.'

> The Delta, *though fertile, is frequently flooded by incoming sea water and is not suitable for rice-growing unless improved by careful irrigation. Impenetrable mangrove swamps cover much of the delta, though many were destroyed by chemical warfare in the 1970's.*

A thought suddenly struck me that if Ha had been born in a war which ended in the middle of the 1970's, how come he was only seven now? It didn't make sense. I felt a moment of disappointment. Perhaps he wasn't a war child after all? Perhaps Patti had got it wrong?

> Bamboo *is the largest form of grass known to man. The shoots are thick and fleshy, and, if picked when young, are often eaten in parts of Eastern Asia. The favourite dish of the river people of the Mekong, is* Laap, *finely chopped duck meat with spices, and rice steamed in a basket.*

Ha nodded his head up and down all the time I was reading, but I don't think he was very interested. Nor was I. So I stopped telling him the boring facts and made up a story about one of the pictures. There was a water-buffalo in the distance, being driven through a wet field by a man in a pointed straw hat. The countryside was green, and in the distance were misty blue hills. My story was about the man planting rice, but since I wasn't too sure how they did it, I skipped over that bit of the story and got quickly to the end.

'So the farmer went home to tea, with his buffalo, and they all lived happily ever after. The end.'

It was obviously going to be harder to teach Ha about the origins of his life than I'd realized.

'There now, Ha, wasn't that a good story?' I closed the book, so he could slide off my lap. But he didn't. Instead, for no reason at all, he suddenly grabbed hold of my hand, seized the little finger and began to bend it backwards as far as it would go.

Scarlet shapes of pain zigzagged in front of me. Ha had my finger in a powerful lock.

'Let go!' I screamed out. 'Ha, what're you *doing? Stop* it!' He pulled harder, twisting so that I could feel the ligament stretching. It hurt so much I couldn't cry but tears sprang to my eyes. Ha suddenly let go, sidled away on his shaky little legs, and sat down amongst the mass of Lego bricks.

I didn't know what to say. I wanted to hit him, to kick him, to smash him in the face, to bend back *his* fingers till they snapped. But I couldn't. Something stopped me. From the way he was sitting there, idly putting one Lego brick on top of another, I had a curious feeling that he didn't realize what he'd done.

I pressed my hand between my thighs to deaden the pain. 'Ha, why did you *do* that? You stupid little boy!' I muttered. 'Don't you realize I'm trying to *help* you?'

He didn't seem to hear, but began to swing his head from side to side, left to right, right to left, swing swing backwards and forwards. Then his shoulders followed the movement, finally his whole body, rocking back and forth, like a pendulum or a mechanical doll. The idiot girl at The Chestnuts had rocked on the floor just like that. So much violent energy in such a small child. And he opened his mouth in a grin, and crowed, high-pitched, like a weird night-bird. His eyes were wide and mad. If only I had known, I'd have seen that they were wide with fear.

I went upstairs, ear-cans on, Vivaldi full volume to blot out

34

thought.

The cat was sleeping on my bed, curled round on the top bunk like a liquorice allsorts whirl. She opened one eye, looked at me, then closed it again. Even if she was only a neutered pet, there was always comfort in being near her. I lay down and stroked her silky back from head to tail.

The seasickness in the night woke me again. I sat up and looked at my watch 3.05 a.m. by the luminous dial. The dead of night and the whole bunk-bed was moving perilously from side to side with nauseous regularity.

I knew now that it must be Ha. But what was he doing? The frame squeaked with each swerve like the parents' bed when they were making love.

Was Ha pleasing himself in the dark of the night?

'Ha!' I shouted down to his bunk. 'You fiddling? Because if you are, it's your privilege. I don't mind what you do to yourself. But kindly do it without waking me too.'

But he was too young. He wouldn't know how. It was a strong movement, more vigorous even than a couple of adults. And adults don't go on and on at it.

'Ha, you're an animal. Stop it!'

Hamsters do it in less than thirty seconds. Quick, rapid activity, and it's all over. Back to sleep. Larger mammals take longer. Lions in season copulate two hundred times over several days, time and again. I reached for the light, and peered over the edge of the bunk-bed. He wasn't fiddling. He was heaving his entire body violently from side to side, like the rocking he'd been doing the day before. But now he was deeply asleep. I climbed down and shook him.

'Ha, wake up. What on earth are you doing?'

He opened his eyes, looked at me, then went back to sleep. The rocking stopped. I climbed back to my bed and curled up. In another minute the rocking began again.

'Ha!' I shouted. 'What are you doing? Please, please stop it. Or I'll go stark raving bonkers.' But however much I shouted, he didn't wake again, and he didn't stop rocking. And at last, in spite of the continuous movement I began to doze off.

'Looky-looky! We found Charlie's little plaything hiding under a bush!'

'What is it?'

35

'That's an AK-47, and a neat little round of ammo with it. And where there's an AK-47, there's Charlie some place near.'

'And we was thinking this ville was so nice and cosy! The sneaky little gook!'

'Yep. And chances are he's right here. And chances are he's got friends.'

'We haven't found him in three nights. So what makes you think we'll find him now?'

'Interrogation time. We make someone do some talky-talky and tell us all about Charlie.'

There's so many ways to make men talk. By water and by fire, by rope and by fear. Drowning or hanging or burning. Either way, you hear them flounder for air to breathe. Either way, you know they're suffocating.

'We can't do it this way, sir. What about the Geneva Convention?'

'I don't give a rat's ass about no Geneva nothing. This is war, sonny.'

'It's daft making these old duffers dangle. They aren't going to say nothing.'

'OK. Cut them down.'

Hearing someone cry hurts more than when you cry yourself. Hearing someone not cry, hurts more than when they do.

5

At night, my head was always full of dark images. I don't fear death, but I fear the moment of dying when your head is thrown back for air ro breathe, reaching for warmth when you're already growing cold.

'Shimoo! Shimoo!' He woke me with the sound of his chanting from the bunk below. He was trying to say my name. 'Shimoo! Shimoo!'

'Well done, Ha,' I said. 'But actually it's not Shimoo. It's Simon. Can you say Si? Then mon?'

'Shimoo!' he said, and went on repeating it as he lay watching me dress. Grey terylene trousers, grey shirt, striped green tie, grey V-neck pullover, grey blazer with new badge. I like uniform. It's more efficient. It saves you having to think too much in the morning. The Old Boy photos in the school hall show they used to wear grey caps too. The school gave them up. I wondered if there'd still be uniform when Ha started. My picture would be up in the hall then. He'd be able to look at it, and be pleased it was me.

When I was ready to go down, he stopped chanting and began to whimper.

'It's OK, Ha. Patti'll be up in a second.'

He had to be bathed every morning, to wash off the pee.

I told them, at breakfast, how he had said my name. 'Well, nearly my name.'

Tony didn't believe me, and Patti was half asleep in her dressing-gown, shovelling soft cereal into Ha's mouth.

'Go on, Ha, you did it upstairs. Si-mon, say it. Si. Si. Si. And then mon.' But however much I coaxed, he wouldn't. Perhaps he was trying to annoy me. He merely stared over the table with those strange, uptilted eyes, with the neat brown skin tightly stretched.

'Gently, Simon, there's a good chap,' said Tony. 'Don't pressurize him. Eat up your own breakfast now.'

Then, just when I was stacking my bowl and mug in the dishwasher, Ha suddenly called across to me. 'Shimoo! Shimoo!' in that high, singsong voice.

I was triumphant. 'You see, Tony!'

Patti poised with the spoon half-way to his mouth and smiled.

'You've really got a way with him, haven't you?' she said.

As I left for school, Ha followed me to the front door and shouted after me, 'Shimoo! Shimoo!' and I almost danced down the street with delight.

My name was the first word he learned. Not Patti. Nor Tony. Nor the cat (whose name was Dido but we never called her anything but Puss.) But me. He said *my* name first. I forgave him trying to bend my little finger. He was only young.

In the afternoon he was at the window watching out for me. I could see him jumping up and down like an excited terrier, his lips moving as he said my name. As I opened the door I heard the chant, 'Shimoo, shimoo, shimoo,' like a mullah calling the faithful to prayer. I realized I'd have to begin teaching him some more words.

My aunt was there, with Sophie and the new baby, and she was making a fuss of Ha's arrival. You'd expect her to, since he's her new nephew, just like we made a fuss at Easter when Ben was born.

My aunt Claire had brought Ha a new box of Lego, and a blue and white stripy sweater, and Sophie's old pushchair.

'It's from Marks and Sparks, Pat. So you can swap it if it doesn't fit. The little sweater, not the buggy. You said small for his age, but you know how misleading the labels can be. And the buggy's pretty battered. We don't want it back. Mike's bought a new one for Ben. First son and all that.'

Claire's younger than Patti and more glamorous and more talkative. She always says: 'And how's my best and favourite nephew?' It's her joke because up till now I've been the only nephew she had.

She chattered on about her battered push-chair. 'I thought after what you said Patti, it might come in useful. You know, if he gets so tired walking. With those funny little legs. D'you suppose they'll improve? Couldn't he have physiotherapy? How's it all working out? In general I mean? Your menfolk behaving all right? God, Pat, you do look rough. You getting enough sleep? And I hope Tony's being a help, and you've —'

Abruptly, she changed the subject and started talking about Sophie's dancing classes.

Sophie's four, and she has a terrible lisp.

'Hello, Thimon,' she said with her head on one side. 'Where hath you been? What hath you been doing, thomething nithe?' Patti says that Claire encourages it.

'Homework,' I said. 'For school.'

'Ith it hard?'

'Yes,' I said, then thought I oughtn't to put her off the idea of school, before she's even started. 'Well no, not really.' I was developing a new technique of getting through my homework very quickly.

Sophie sat on the floor with the new box of Lego and started to make an elaborate structure.

'Ith a faiwy palath,' she said.

'What?' I said.

'For the faiwy queen.'

'Oh I see.' Her fairy palace was cleverly constructed, with pinnacles and turrets, and cantilevered steps. Ha sat down beside her and propped two Lego bricks on top of each other. I'd shown him how Lego bricks click together, but he hadn't got the knack of it yet.

Sophie's fairy palace grew magnificently upwards. I thought Ha was going to knock it over, but he only stared.

'D'you want to play a game now, Sophie?' I said. 'I'll teach you draughts if you like.'

'Wath that?'

'A game.' We put the fairy palace up on the shelf and I set out the black and white board on the floor. Sophie picked up the moves very rapidly. I let her win the first two games. Then the third game, I didn't give her any advantages, but she still played well, considering she'd never done it before, and she didn't make a fuss when she lost.

Ha watched us. I showed him how to play too. But it was very frustrating. He didn't seem able to get the idea of how the counters move diagonally across the board, or what I meant by huffing or queening. He shoved them about at random, or piled them on top of each other.

So I played a couple of more games with Sophie, while Ha gazed at the board in a sort of trance, as though the squares of black and white was the most absorbing pattern in the world. Then, just as Sophie and I were starting another game, Ha deliberately shoved the counters out of the way, seized hold of the board, and held it up to his face.

And suddenly I realized what it was about Ha. He wasn't normal mentally. I felt terrible, almost ill.

As Ha scattered the counters Sophie looked as though she was going to burst into tears. Luckily, the baby in the carry-cot began to wail, and Aunt Claire said it was time for them to be off. She said what a saint I was, and what a lucky boy Ha was to have me for his big brother, and how truly marvellous I was with small children, and did I ever want a job looking after hers?

None of her flattery made me feel any better.

When they'd left, Patti sat Ha down in front of the television, and went to make bread. I followed her to the kitchen.

'There's something wrong with him,' I said. A sort of question. I didn't know for certain that there was. I wanted *her* to tell *me*.

Patti glanced up. 'What's that, darling?' and went on kneading. Thump, thump, knuckles into sticky dough, pummelling hard. She doesn't usually have time for bread during the week.

'Lay the table for supper, Simon, would you, darling? Don't forget Ha's bib. There's a clean one in the drawer. And I got him a new dish today. It's in the hall.'

I fetched her shopping basket. Going through the shopping is sometimes good fun, like undoing a Christmas stocking. But there was nothing surprising today. A bag of leeks. A pair of orange rubber gloves. A packet of disposable nappies, large size. And a new, unbreakable, plastic bowl. Printed round the rim, more bunnies, these ones wearing spotted bow-ties. It had a large rubber suction pad underneath so that you could stick it to a smooth surface. I pulled the bowl from its cellophane wrapping and tried it out on the polished table. Once stuck down with a dab of lick and lots of pressure, there was no way it would budge. It was amazing. He wouldn't be able to throw *that* across the room.

'Better wash it before it's used,' Patti said.

'It can't be dirty! It was all wrapped up. Airproof. No germs could possibly get in.'

But I gave it a quick wipe with a cloth since she wanted me to, then I laid the table. Usual stuff, plus wineglasses for the parents. They've taken to having a glass of wine every day now. Two spoons and a fork for Ha, not that he ever bothers to use them.

'There *is* something wrong with him,' I said as I fetched the salt and pepper. 'Isn't there?'

'Of course there is,' Patti snapped. She never snapped, especially not when cooking. She loves cooking. She used to say that it was her way of unwinding after work. But she hardly needed to unwind. She hadn't *been* to work since Ha came. 'You know perfectly well, Simon, that he's not normal. If he was an ordinary little boy, who'd always grown up with two parents, in a proper family, he wouldn't *be* here, now would he? Socially, he's been very deprived. He was totally institutionalized in that Home. He needs the therapy of love.'

She was beginning to sound like Miss Spaark.

'I know all about that. You've already told me about his poor sad past. I mean something *more*. That game of draughts I played with him and Sophie. He didn't even get the first *clue*!'

Sophie was always alert, listening all the time, and copying, trying things out. Ha wasn't like that. He was just switched off. 'Even if you explain things again and again, he just doesn't catch on.'

'Sophie's very precocious for her age,' said Patti. 'It's the way Claire treats her, like a miniature grown-up.'

She finished kneading the dough, rolled it into three strands, floured them, wove them into a plait, brushed the plait with milk, and sprinkled the top with black poppy seeds.

'He's got something wrong in the head, hasn't he? He's got a screw loose.'

'I don't know what you mean.' She seemed quite angry.

'Come on, mother. You know exactly what I'm driving at.' I didn't want to say it, but I had to because she wouldn't. 'There's another word we use at school. Dum-dum. He's a dum-dum, isn't he?'

'Please, Simon, don't use that awful word in this house!' she said, and she banged into the neat plait with her fist clenched so that her pretty work was all undone, and the seeded bread spread into a shapeless mass.

Her violence made me feel violent. I banged both my hands on to the dough and shouted at her.

'Is he a dum-dum or not? That's all I want to know. And if he is what are you going to do about it?'

She just shook her head and started crying into her squashed loaf.

'You knew when we went to fetch him, didn't you? So why him? Why not choose one of the others?'

'Simon, don't go on. It's too difficult to explain. Don't you see, we just have to *love* him. What else is there?' And she flung her floury arms round my neck and hugged me so tightly I could hardly breathe and I wanted her to go on squeezing me against her until I suffocated.

She released me abruptly and fetched the pedal bin and began to scrape the smashed dough into it, even though she hates waste. She even saves old vegetable parings to make stock.

'Don't throw it away,' I said. I felt ashamed of my part in its destruction. 'I'm sure you could make it all right.'

Obediently she began moulding the dough back into shape.

6

Just to survive through a single day, he needed so much attention. To make sure he didn't starve because he couldn't feed himself, didn't drown because he couldn't bath himself, didn't break his neck because he got shit-scared coming downstairs, didn't strangle himself in his vest because he couldn't dress himself, didn't die of utter boredom because he'd no way of thinking for himself.

His shorts always had a dark damp stain at the front. His pants were always smeared. A plastic bin of soiled garments stood brimming in the bathroom. The cat used to go and sniff at it for pleasure.

So much for the blue plastic pot under the bed. He hadn't a clue what it was for.

I wanted answers to questions. What was going to happen to him? Why was he like that? What did they want him for?

'Guilt,' said Tony. 'I suppose. About the war.'

'But you had nothing to do with it. You needn't feel guilty.'

'Of course we needn't. But we do. Collective guilt. We may not actually *be* guilty. But we're all responsible.'

That was not the answer I wanted.

Patti's answers were just as evasive.

'It's early days yet. It'll be all right in the end. It's going to take time. Miss Spaark says it's amazing he's developing so well.'

What did Miss Spaark know about anything? She didn't have to live with the wetting, the dribbling, the stupid, aimless playing with bits of string, the staring vacantly into space with his mouth open, the sneaky pinching at my skin with his horrible yellow fingernails.

He was fed by Patti, read to by Patti, washed by Patti, put to bed by Patti. Me and Tony saw to the rest of the house, so nothing was as it used to be. Supper was late and usually burned.

'Faintly caramelized,' Tony said, of our cauliflower cheese. 'But not a bad first effort.'

I got used to it. Get through the meal as quick as pos., and bolt upstairs before they started trying to teach Ha to use the spoon and fork. Did they argue about *me* when they were bringing me up? I doubted it. I was an ordinary baby who matched the pictures in the book. I wasn't a dum-dum war orphan.

However, it wasn't really any of my problem. A child had come into our home who was a joey. Tough luck. I'd survive. The bit I really minded was when the cat took to sleeping on *his* bed.

Our cat. My cat. Part of the family since the day I was one. There was a photograph in the album of me in a frilly baby outfit sitting with the fluffy kitten on a tartan rug on the lawn, all cute-eyed and delicate nose and white whiskers. When I was three or four I used to dress her up in teddy clothes and carry her about in a basket and call her my sister. And she's been part of our life ever since. As she's grown older, she's tended to sleep more. In the afternoon, when I came home from school, she's usually been sleeping peacefully in the middle of my bed.

And then, in one day, her loyalty switched. Not my bed, but his. She's only a cat, but it hurt like pain. My black coil of a cat on *his* bunk-bed, nestling amongst the patterned bunnies of *his* covers. I know why she changed beds. The cat likes the stink of Ha's bed. The animal smell of urine which lingers even after the sheets have been changed.

I didn't hate the poor old cat for her betrayal. I hated Ha. I'd never really loved him. I'd only wanted to please my parents. All my life I've tried to impress Tony. I'd never got it right.

'Patti, what happens if it doesn't work out? If we don't like it?'

'What d'you mean?'

'If we decide that Ha doesn't really fit in?'

'It has to work. What are the alternatives?'

'Well, what would happen if one of his proper parents were alive somewhere trying to *find* him?'

'It's a very remote possibility. It would be very difficult, I should think.'

'I know. But *could* they? If they were determined?'

Tony looked over the top of his paper. 'Don't nag your mother, Simon.'

'It's all right, Tony. He's entitled to ask.'

Tony put his paper down. 'Very well. Yes, Simon, it just might be possible. The Red Cross sometimes helps. And you do hear of miraculous thousand-to-one chances of people meeting up. Some of the Boat people were reunited. But Miss Spaark has assured us we needn't expect any complications in this case.'

At last, Ha started school. It was the other side of town.

'Special school for a special boy,' said Patti, shoving his arms

44

into his anorak and zipping him in. She hung his school-bag gently over his shoulder with his gym-shoes and his dinner-money. Patti put two coloured felt-tips and a note-pad in as well, to make it seem as though he had real things. To be like me.

'I'm going to be late. Bye, Patti,' I said.

'It's only twenty to. You don't usually leave till ten past.'

So I had to wait with Ha by the front door till his bus came. He tried to imitate the way I stood. I slung my bag down to my feet. Ha did the same. I whistled nonchalently. He pursed his lips.

'Sch boo,' he said, pointing down to our bags.

I nodded. Want to do a swap, poor little imbecile. You have my Latin, my chemistry, my calculator. I'll have your two felt-tips.

The mini-bus pulled up in front of our house, and the driver hooted loudly. Through the windows peered children with lolling tongues, jiggering heads, and groping, palsied hands. One boy, near the door, looked almost the same as Ha, with slanting eyes and snubby nose. He was a mongol. I hoped none of the people across the road were watching.

He waved to me as Patti helped him stagger up the steps.

'Shimoo, bye!' he said.

'Pay, pay, pay!' he wailed. 'Gimme pay!'

He meant my drawing paper. One day I'd given him a page of my rough book. He became obsessive about drawing. Tony brought home a boxful of used computer paper. It had print-out on one side, but the other side was usually blank and could be used for drawing.

Occasionally, the paper had print-out on both sides, a single column of figures down one margin. He would never use it if it had printing on more than one side. If he was offered a sheet with even one word where he expected it to be blank, he tore it up angrily, threw it in the bin, and demanded a fresh piece.

'All right, I'm getting it.'

It came in a continuous roll with perforations marking each sheet. Ha couldn't master the simple manual technique of tearing himself off a sheet when he needed it, but clamoured for help.

Ha always drew the same picture. It was a large square vehicle with eight wheels. He used a black felt-tip pen, so that the drawing had heavy outlines. I tried to show him how to use a soft 3B to get the different levels of shading. He wasn't interested. He preferred his solid black lines. And after he'd drawn his eight-wheeled truck, he always scribbled all over the page, like a rainstorm, so that the drawing became totally obscured.

Then, he drew something new. It was a plane. It was enormous. It filled the whole page, from side to side, top to bottom. A small spider figure appeared underneath, looking up. He'd not drawn people before. He showed me the tiny man.

'Day,' he said.

'What?'

'Dy day. Him day.'

'Say it slower.'

'Him dy. Kill him. Him cry. He him cry day.'

'Oh. You mean he's dead? He doesn't look very dead,' I said. 'He's standing up, on legs. If he was dead, he'd be lying down.'

He shook his head. 'No. No. No. No.' He always said 'No' four times. It wasted a lot of time, waiting for him to get through his four No's. Do you want custard on your pie, Ha? No. No. No. No.

'Killing him. No. No. No. No. Day him big dat him killing him. Dat man him me. Big noy bang.'

It could take hours trying to work out his nonsensical language. I didn't bother. Sometimes I switched off. Sometimes I just guessed.

'You know Patti, Ha ought to be taught to talk properly,' I said. 'Then you wouldn't have to do everything for him all the time, and I'd understand what he was saying.' I'd seen the mongol on his bus talking, in a slow, slurred way. 'Even the dum-dums can learn to communicate.'

'Simon, please. Not that awful expression.'

'What d'you want me to say? A joey, a flid, a spazzy?'

'Retarded, owing to brain damage. And he's going to have speech therapy as soon as it can be arranged.'

'Good. Glad to hear it.'

Ha tugged at my sleeve to show me his masterpiece.

'Him day. Killing, yeah, see me him, deah him dead kill.'

I got the message, roughly speaking. The big plane was killing the tiny spiderman which was meant to be Ha. I explained to Ha the overall lack of logic in his pictorial story. The plane couldn't have killed Ha, because Ha was still very much alive, and here. Worse luck.

His plane had a sharp, needle nose, pointing forward like an insect's proboscis, and wide, swept-back wings. Ha grabbed a red felt-tip pen and scribbled red lights on the underside of the plane and at the tips of the wings. Then he took the black again and blacked in the whole plane so that it was like a dark silhouette against the sky.

Ha's drawing was creepy. I didn't want to look at it any more.

I switched on the television for him. He loved watching television, especially violence. But whenever he watched, he went out of control. He laughed when the detective slumped, riddled with bullets, against the wall. He fell sideways with mirth when the car burst into flames and plunged over the cliff. It sickened me.

'By the way, darling,' said Patti. 'Tony said he'd really like to go out to a film this evening. After supper. If you'll go with him?' She was forcing good cheer into her voice.

'What about you?'

'I'll stay here. I've got lots to catch up on. I'm going back to work next week.'

I don't know if it was really Tony's idea to take me to the cinema. He kept falling asleep in the exciting bits, and then waking up with a jolt and saying how much he was enjoying it. But he made it into a real treat, like a birthday outing or half-term, giving me money for popcorn, and pepsi, and chocolate. All the junk food. And a boiled rubber hot dog in the intermission, and I felt that they did love me best, even if we'd never be able to be together as a proper family any more.

It was a very long film. We weren't home till after eleven. Ha was already tucked up and asleep so I had to move quietly. He whimpered in his sleep, like a dog dreaming of going down an earthy rabbit hole. The air smelled warm and dank, of rotting leaves and flesh, with the crackle of burning. The heavy voices came at me through the dark.

> 'Why do we have to do this, sir? That jungle ain't doing nobody any harm, sir.'

There were four men in my bedroom, speaking to one another. Or was it I who had left my bedroom and gone somewhere else?

> 'We gotta deprive them of lodging and food throughout this area. You ask too many questions, sonny. We have to prevent Charlie moving about any place. We evacuate civilians, then anything else in there that moves is hostile.'
>
> 'Even the monkeys, sir?'
>
> 'Sure. I'm telling you, even the cats and dogs round here are VC!'

They drifted away into laughter, and the rocking began. I lay in the hammock swaying gently from side to side. My grandmother's hammock hung between two mulberry trees, in her garden. The air was scented with fruit blossom, and I saw a flock of white egrets against the sky. Then Ha spoiled it all by screaming, high-pitched as though he was being strangled. He wouldn't stop. Lights went on in the passage. The parents had heard it too, staggering through sleep to appear in the lighted doorway like night ghosts. My father had no pyjamas. Was it the fire of love or war which had unclothed him? He disappeared into the shadows and Patti came to me with calming noises, and soft maternal comfort. The screaming went on.

She held me in her arms, my head against her, crooning sweet noises at me.

'It's all right, darling. It's all right,' she said like a breeze in my ear. And gradually the screaming subsided. It was coming from my throat, not his.

At breakfast (tea, toast, cereal, but no juice and no eggs because Tony and I forgot to buy any) I thought they'd say something. I wanted them to say something about the night. They didn't even mention it. It was all Ha this, Ha that. Don't they know I'm here too?

I was attacked again by the same boys. They must have been the same ones, though they all look alike. But I was in a hurry to get home. Not for love. But to see what he'd done today.

'Get lost, flids,' I screamed at the boy whose hand was fastened round my neck. 'You stupid pin-head burk.' I think I kicked him, then ran, and fast.

The atmosphere in the house was electric. I felt it immediately, like barbs zagging through the skin. Something had happened. Ha squatted, in his quaint oriental fashion, before the television, in obeisance to his new god. But there was no violence on at 4.15 so he had to make do with *Playschool*, cuddly Humpty, and the carefree antics of adult actors pretending to be toddlers.

'What you watching that crap for? Bit unsuitable for you, isn't it, that kind of placid rubbish?'

Patti was in the kitchen, marking exercise books, like old times. In a moment, she'd say, 'Hello darling, tea in the pot. Nice day? Much homework? Supper about seven, all right?'

She looked like a body washed up on the shore. She had

48

pinched lines running from her nose to her chin. My mother had turned into an old witch-woman. Her hair was a mess like knitting-wool. Once, long ago, I used to have a beautiful mother, with long, glossy hair and a serene smile radiating peace over the household. No 'Hello darling.' Just a blank stare.

'Well?' I said. 'What is it? What's he done?'

'Outside, Simon. I'm sorry.' She shook her head.

A weeping mother is the last thing you need in a time of unidentified crisis. Didn't she realize that those essays on 'Nutritional Values of Dairy Products' had been written, with care, by schoolchildren like me. It showed little respect to go sobbing all over them.

'Outside where?' I threw down my bag. Eng. Lit., Hist., Biol., crossed the kitchen, picking up a coconut crunchie on the way, to the back door.

It all looked normal in the yard. The coal bunker still in position, the forsythia in place, the stack of wood, the hose-pipe neatly rolled on a hook, the faded indoor pot plants put out to breathe along the wall. What did she want me to see? Had he broken a couple of buds off her favourite bush?

Then I saw the cat. Our cat. My cat, who I've known since I was one. It was on the crazy paving, its four limbs spread out. A flat cat. I looked up to the window. She must have fallen, or been thrown, just as he once threw my slippers, and his toy rabbit, and my Parker 45. A cat has nine lives. I saw a diagram, once, demonstrating the way a falling cat rights itself, by means of its tail. My cat had used all nine lives in one short flight. Or perhaps he had strangled it first, or bent its little paws back, or stabbed it with a pencil.

She hadn't done anything about it, just left it there. I wasn't surprised.

I took the fish-slice and the coal-shovel to scoop it up. Only then, I didn't know what to do with it. So I had to put it down again. I couldn't put the cat in the bin. Ha's disposable nappies go in there, wait all week just outside the back door, till the bin men come on Wednesdays. I dug a hole in the flower-bed beside Patti's rose-bush, wrapped the cat in newspaper, and tried to put it in the hole, but its legs and tail stuck out and I had to dig the hole much bigger before the whole of the cat could be buried. I hoped the bacterial breakdown would be quick.

Ha had a criss-cross of inflamed red scratches across his face and hands. I was glad that the cat had, at least, put up good resistance.

I went upstairs to my room. But of course it wasn't my room any more. It was our room, and becoming more his room every day. His Lego, his crumpled books, his hoard of empty cereal packets saved for no purpose, his wet pants, his scribbling on the wall, his smell. And his destruction of the anniversary wallpaper. He had found it in the bottom drawer. He had shredded it into strips. I didn't even care. Compared to the cat, the spoiling of a few bits of decorated paper was nothing.

He'd be bound to go now. When a child murders a cat, there's really something wrong. Next thing it might be people he'd start killing.

I slotted in Vivaldi, put the cans over my ears, and planned my essay: introduction, three main points, conclusion, carefully underlining each heading.

But even Vivaldi and homework couldn't block him out. Sounds of screaming floated upstairs, and were soon too intense to be ignored.

Slowly, I went down. In the hall, Ha and Patti appeared to be wrestling. He was grappling with the doorknob, at the same time Patti was trying to prevent him going out. He was shrieking, kicking and biting. She was making calming noises.

'Come on, Ha, it's all right. Let's find out what's wrong, and make it better.'

I could see one thing that was wrong. He'd pooed in his pants, and all down his legs. I didn't know how she could bear to touch him.

'It's all right, Ha. We love you,' she said. 'Where d'you want to go? Let mummy clean you up, then I'll take you.'

He was deaf to endearments. He heard nothing, saw nothing. He began to beat his head hard against the door, like a hammer.

Then we heard Tony's key in the latch. Ha stopped screaming and sank to the floor as though his legs had collapsed under him. Screaming turned to whimpering, and he grovelled at Tony's feet like a cowering dog.

I felt so angry. Tony had merely to walk in through the door, and Ha's tantrum was deflated.

'Well, well, and what set this little scene off?' said Tony trying to pick Ha up.

Patti started to explain about the cat, which set Ha off again.

Between them they managed to get him up to the bathroom. The clean-up, first Ha, then the hall, took hours. I kept out of the way. I heard their voices raised, arguing. They never used to argue.

At half-past seven I went into the kitchen and found Tony making a pot of tea but no sign of supper. The hall smelled of Dettol, and Ha, in pyjamas, smelled of talcum powder. I could see exactly where Patti had scrubbed the carpet. The wool pile was fluffier, the colour brighter then the rest, and always would be. No amount of rubbing and mopping could ever remove the signs and stains of Ha from our house.

'Like to carry this up to your mother?' said Tony. 'She's not feeling too well, as you can imagine. Gone to bed with a couple of paracetamol.'

I carried up the tray. But the curtains were drawn, and the room dim. I wanted to crawl in with her like I used to when I was four, and be warm against her and feel her against me, and comfort her and never come out into the world again.

'Patti?' I whispered. 'I've brought you some tea.' No reply.

'Tea,' I said louder. Silence. Either she was asleep or pretending. I carried the tray down.

'Fish and chips tonight,' said Tony. He gave me a fiver to go and fetch them from the chippie, and we ate in silence straight out of the polystyrene cartons. Tony fed flakes of cod into Ha's mouth, but Ha managed to feed the chips to himself. Tony should have been pleased by this development in Ha's progress. But I don't think he even noticed.

I had to help Tony fix on Ha's bedtime nappy because he didn't know how. Ha lay obediently on his back on the lower bunk with his legs out, while I showed Tony which way round the plastic pants go. Then Ha went to bed sweet and docile as a little lamb, offering his rosy cheek for a good-night kiss.

'Hope you won't mind, Simon, if I hit the sack too?' It was only half-past eight. 'That sort of scene is totally gruelling. There's probably something good you could watch on the box.' He gave me the evening paper from his brief case, said good-night, then came back. 'By the way, I'm very sorry about Dido, really I am.'

'What? Oh. Dido, yes.' She'd never really been Dido.

'But it was probably very quick. I don't suppose she had time to suffer.'

I nodded.

'We can't punish him for it. He wouldn't understand. I think he's probably punished himself.'

It may have left them exhausted. It left me angry, all keyed up

51

like before a match.

If I'd kept Miss Spaark's number, I would have rung her and told her about the cat. Then we could get back to where we were before. The loving trio we were meant to be. But I'd work something out. I'm a high IQ, High School boy. It wasn't beyond me to find the means.

I turned on the telly, but the programme was hardly worth watching. I put on one of Tony's records. It was grating discordant music, just what he liked.

I went into the kitchen, found a packet of chocolate wafers and ate them, two at a time. Then I looked in the cupboard in the sitting-room beside the bookshelf. There were bottles of port, gin, curaçao, Noilly Prat, an inch or two left in each. So I fetched a glass, and some ice and mixed a marvellous cocktail. It was an astonishing colour, tasted vile, and gave a wonderful sensation of floating. The moving light on the television began to seem entertaining. Tony's music began to sound harmonious. I began to feel better, and had the inspiration that a smoke would complete the evening.

I opened the bureau and searched through the drawers. Postage stamps, rubber bands, paper-clips, bills paid and unpaid, bank statements. Somewhere in there was a packet of filter-tips, a left-over pack from the days when Patti was a smoker, before she got scared of dying. She kept it as a talisman.

But instead of filter-tips, I found a beige-coloured file. It was crammed with letters, documents, typed reports, all referring to one child.

NGUYEN THANH HA (ROBERT) child; male, I read, because the file wasn't marked private or confidential.

DISABILITY: low IQ, physically retarded. Malnutrition, rickets, T.B., dental caries.

PARENTS: unknown. Thought to have originated in the province of Quoc Suc: hamlet possibly eradicated in land resettlement.

The reports went back over several years.

Backward but appealing,

He is making progress.

MENTAL AGE: Currently assessed at half chronological age. Good progress in communication, walking and in some day-to-day skills.

Then the reports stopped being so optimistic.

Tests for deafness are to be run. May be visually handicapped.
Marked deterioration in overall condition.
Recommended reassessment biannually.

These bald facts were, no doubt, all very fascinating to Patti and Tony. But what leaped out at me, and danced and swam on and off the page, was my own birthdate, clearly typed across the top of each report. My day, month and year of birth. Why should my parents have wanted to hang on to this kind of unflattering account about me and my progress?

But it wasn't about me. Of course it couldn't be. It was Nguyen Thanh Ha (Robert). It said so.

Nguyen Thanh Ha (Robert) had taken everything from me, my bedroom, my privacy, my freedom. Now, he'd even stolen my birthday.

I mixed myself another cocktail, this time more Noilly Prat, less Coffee Liqueur Creme.

I half wished I'd never looked in that bureau. I'd rather not have known that they kept a bulging file of information on their special, chosen child. I'd rather not have known that they'd lie to me about him, pretending they didn't know things about him which they did. Of course, I suspected all along that he was no babe in the wood. But till then I'd never really thought about him growing up, just like me. He wasn't tall, but he had enormous feet. And he had something else too.

Until I was quite old, Patti always used to stay with me in the bathroom and sit on the edge of the bath and chat while I was washing. I suppose she was afraid I might drown if I was on my own. But now I always bath with the door locked. And I've looked all over my body for hairs. So far, I've only found fluff. But when Ha was lying down to have his nappy put on, I saw that he's already got black hair growing.

I have nearly reached the beginning of adult life. Hormones are coursing through my body, changing me into a man. I am a rational, thinking person, growing in wisdom and knowledge every day. I understand about things. I know French and Latin. I'm in the upper maths group.

But it isn't his fault that he's my twin. It's *theirs*. *They* are the liars, the cheats, the defrauders.

I kicked the beige file on to the carpet and two snapshots slipped out.

Patti once showed me a picture of her father before he died. I hadn't recognized myself as a three-year-old, yet I'd known from the glimpse of the garden chair which my grandmother still has, where the photograph was taken, and from the bright spots of daisies on the lawn, that it was spring. And though I didn't really remember what Patti's father looked like, I knew from these clues that the old man beside the small child was my grandfather.

I looked in these two photographs for similar background clues which I might recognize. But there seemed no key points to help with identifying them. The light was wrong, the clothes wrong, the building unknown. All I could see in the background was a leafless tree, a louvred doorway, a rush-mat and a wall of flaking plaster. One snapshot showed a row of scraggy Asian waifs with shaven heads, sitting on a wooden bench in a dusty yard. The other showed a European woman holding two small children in her arms. Both were unfamiliar, foreign scenes, probably taken in Ha's country.

The woman was wearing a skimpy cotton dress and open sandals. On the floor beside her, and around her sitting or sprawling on the black and white chequered tiles, were more children. I counted them. There were thirteen of them, all with spindly limbs and vacant eyes, looking like drowned baby birds with no cheep left.

Then, I suddenly recognized what was important about the pictures. One of the children, stranded on the mat, his legs sticking straight out like sticks, naked except for a short smock with two rips in it hanging loose on his body, was Ha. A different Ha from now, frail and emaciated as an old, old man, and with a vacant, ghostly face, but undeniably him. And the young woman holding the two babies was Patti.

What was she doing in Ha's country?

7

I was going to storm upstairs and shout at them, pull them from their bed, demand explanations. But any answers they gave were bound to be false.

Instead, I lurched out of the house, slammed the front door and waited. When the reverberations woke them, they'd come running down and plead with me to stay.

But nobody stirred. So I had to grope my way off down the road. I was red hot and angry.

I walked through the shopping precinct, looked at the models in the dress shop windows and wondered why they bothered to keep so many lights on when there was nobody about. I walked down the High Street to the medieval tower which used to be the city gates, then out towards the ring road. Lorries from the ferryport thundered past, and when I tried to cross over the road, I misjudged their speed, and I didn't seem able to get over in a straight, direct line. The second time I stepped off the kerb, an articulated truck flashed its headlamps and swerved over to the far side, but it was still close enough to buffet me with wind turbulence. When a police patrol cruised past, for some reason I ducked behind the metal crash barrier, and crouched as low as I could like a soldier hiding in the dark in his own foxhole.

But I had done nothing wrong. It was they who had wronged me with their lies and pretence and treachery. What was Patti doing in that picture? Where was Tony? Where was I?

After the police car, I left the main road and followed a track through the orchards. It was dark and the apple branches seemed to close over my head, shutting out even the orange glow from the town. At the unmanned railway crossing, I was more careful than I'd been on the city ring road and I listened for the sound of trains, but there are no trains after half-past eleven. The walking and the cold woke me up and I saw that I was heading out towards Aunt Claire's village. It's always seemed a quick ride by car, no more than five or six minutes. On foot, in the night, it seemed to take for ever, and I stumbled into puddles and bumped into hedges.

I reached the post office in the middle of her village and the pub. Aunt Claire lives in a timbered cottage, set below the level of the lane, down three brick steps. There were no lights even after

I'd knocked, so I walked all round the cottage, slipping on the moss, and I tried to find a way in. At the back, I saw somebody dart behind an outhouse, but when I went after them, it turned out to be washing on a line left out in the dark.

They had to be there and they had to let me in because I was cold, and tired, and I was beginning to have a headache. I banged again loudly on the front door and threw some sticks up at one of the latticed windows. Why wouldn't they wake up? I was not going to let everybody ignore me like this.

I jogged back to the phone-box outside the post office. It was dimly lit and smelled, like Ha's mattress, of stale urine.

I dialled my aunt's number. It rang for a long time. At last it was picked up at the other end, and the ringing tone changed to rapid bleeps. But I had no money. So I replaced the receiver, then immediately dialled the number again. It was answered more quickly this time. Just to make quite certain they were properly awake, I dialled one more time, then I ran as fast as I was able back through the village, down the lane to the cottage before they could have time to fall asleep. I knocked hard on the front door, again and again.

Lights went on in no time. The window overhead opened and Uncle Mike's face appeared.

'What the hell d'you want?' he roared. 'Whoever you are?'

'It's me.' My voice seemed small.

'For God's sake, what time d'you think it is? Who are you down there?'

'It's Simon. Patti's son.'

The name must have flicked something on in his sleepy brain. 'Oh. You.'

'Is Aunt Claire in?' My voice seemed to have totally disintegrated.

'Of course she's in! In bed. Where d'you expect her to be? What are you doing down there anyway?' He disappeared inside the folds of the curtain, then the window closed.

It was an inconclusive exchange and I wasn't sure if he was coming down or not. In the end, I realized he wasn't.

I was twenty yards along the lane, when Aunt Claire appeared behind me, running along in high-heeled slippers and a white frilly dressing-gown. 'Simon, come back. Where on earth d'you think you're going?'

Uncle Mike was up by now and he made a pot of tea.

'Now what on earth is all this?' said my aunt. 'Does Pat know you're out on the rampage?'

'Yes,' I said. 'Of course. She thinks I'm with a school friend.'

'What rubbish. She doesn't think any such thing. You haven't even come out with enough proper clothes. You're blue with cold. Look at you.'

She seemed to be laughing at me rather than annoyed.

Her husband fetched me an Aran sweater and made me put it on and began to rake out the grey ashes in the grate, and make up a fire.

'You must ring her and tell her where you are. She'll be out of her mind with worry.'

'She wasn't when I left. She was asleep. They both were. They won't even notice.'

'Don't be silly, Simon. You may think she doesn't care, but she does. And if you won't ring, then I will.'

'I don't want to go back,' I said.

'Ever?' She was holding the phone.

'I don't know.'

'Hello, Pat? No, he's all right. No, he's not drunk.' She glanced over at me with her eyebrows up. 'Why? Is he meant to be? No, fine. I've never seen him look so well. No, of course not.'

When somebody's having a telephone conversation about you, in the same room, it's very hard not to listen. Claire's husband, blowing on the flames, was listening too. 'Yes, all right, and Mike'll drive him back in the morning. Don't worry. Bye, darling. Oh yes, and Simon says he's very sorry indeed to have worried you. He didn't mean to.' She looked sternly across the room at me as she said this. 'He just wanted a bit of a breather. He's such a sweetie, isn't he. Bye now, sleep well.' She rang off, satisfied. 'You see! Of course they knew you'd gone. They were worried stiff. And very glad to be reassured.'

Uncle Mike put a guard round the fire, then said he'd go up. He came and patted my shoulder. 'Night, old boy. Glad you came. Better than out in the cold, hm?'

He's a peculiar man. Claire refilled my cup from the pot. 'Now what's all this about? I suppose it's because of the little boy?'

'There's things I ought to know, which they haven't told me.'

'It's not been easy for them either. But you'll find you can accept it in the end. I expect you know, Pat and I had a little sister who wasn't quite like other children, a Down's Syndrome baby?'

I hadn't known. It was one more piece of hidden truth.

'She died when she was three. They often did in those days. I sometimes think that's why Pat wanted Ha so much. To make up for not being able to look after little Liz. It's a terrible thing having a handicapped brother or sister. But it's even worse if they're taken away.'

'It's not him being dopey I mind most. It's *them*. They lied to me. I found all the stuff in the desk.'

My aunt is often very silly but for some reason I trusted her. She settled herself down on the end of the sofa as though she was about to read me a bedtime story. 'Well?' she said. 'What d'you want to know?'

'Anything you know.'

'Well,' she began, 'your mother first got involved after she lost a child. A miscarriage, if you know what that is. A baby dies before it's born. She didn't seem to get over it, until one day she was sitting crying as usual and she heard about an appeal for trained volunteers. They really wanted nurses, but nutrition experts were needed too. Our mother — Granny — tried to stop her going out there. But Tony thought it might help. In a way, I think it did; seeing so many other children in need stopped her thinking about herself. I remember she wrote a postcard to me, "The place is full of dead babies, so many you can't even count them. They die so quickly here. But I suppose it's better that way."'

'Why did she want to go off to look after other people's children when she already had me?'

'They weren't exactly other people's children. They didn't belong to anybody.'

'They must have!' I said. Children don't just spring from nowhere, even I know that. They must have had parents at the beginning.

'Lots were simply abandoned. There were dozens of orphanages where she was. And altogether literally thousands of orphans. Nobody could sort all that lot out in the middle of a war. There was an abandoned baby girl she looked after, who she wanted to bring home. I don't know what happened. I suppose it died.'

'Where was I?'

'You were on holiday. A month with me, then a month with your granny. Your father came every weekend.'

I remembered the holiday at the seaside. Long sunlit days on the sand, digging trenches and making castles as the tide went out. Granny bought me a metal gardening trowel which was better for digging than a plastic spade. One evening, she and I had sat on the rocks till nearly nine o'clock, waiting for the tide to turn and to surge inland, and fill the channels, and smash into my fortifications. Then by next morning, the ripple of the waves had completely smoothed over all the sand, so that there were no traces left of where my buildings had been.

And I hadn't known that, while I was playing with the sand, my mother had been to the edge of a war on the other side of the world. I wondered how I could have been so ignorant and so blind, not to have noticed what they'd been up to behind my back.

'And when Patti's visa expired, she came back. And that was the end of that. She'd got over the pain of losing her own baby. And it was back to ordinary life. Except that she didn't ever talk to anybody about her time out there.'

'And she didn't bring Ha back with her?'

'No, he was just one of many children in the place where she worked. But then, just before the war was ending, lots of the children were airlifted out, to Australia, America, Canada, Switzerland. All over the place.'

'What for?'

'I think they thought they'd all be killed by the enemy. A newspaper paid for one of the airlifts, as a sort of publicity stunt. Anyway, we saw a picture of a group who'd arrived here and your mother thought she recognized one of them from the orphanage she'd stayed in. She traced him and went to see him, but she wasn't sure if he was the same child because he'd changed so much. She and Tony decided to sponsor him anyway, who-ever he was.'

I didn't know what sponsoring was.

'People paid money for the upkeep of a child, so it was like "their" child. But apart from sending the money, they didn't have to have anything to do with it if they didn't want to.'

'How much?'

'I don't know. Whatever it costs to keep a child. You know, really your mother should be telling you all this, not me.'

So that was why we never moved to the house with the big garden, never got the new car, stopped going to France on holiday, never did anything except live out our quiet, wholesome life. And the ten-speed racer I might have had to save me walking to school had presumably gone on feeding Ha.

'So why did she suddenly want to adopt him, if she didn't have to?'

'It wasn't sudden. It was very gradual. They started visiting him in the Home. But instead of improving, she was convinced he was getting worse. His only hope, they thought, was to be in a family with proper attention and love. It was a risk she took, and, unfortunately, it seems to have gone a bit wrong. My sister's a brave person. Misguided perhaps, but at least she always *tries* to do the right thing.'

'But it hasn't gone wrong,' I said. 'The only bit that went wrong was them not *telling* me! I'd have understood. Now I know, it's all beginning to make sense. And it'll be the same for Ha. At the moment, he just lives in a sort of violent blur. If they tell him the truth about his past, his life can begin to make sense.'

'Simon, Ha's mind is damaged. Most of his life is *never* going to make sense. You must accept it, and just try to love him as he is.'

She and Patti were always going on about loving, when it's *truth* that matters.

'Doesn't Patti care about who he was before? Didn't she try to find out anything? Just because bad things might have happened to him, it doesn't mean everybody should pretend nothing at all happened.' My stupid parents didn't seem to understand the first thing about him. 'The past is terribly important. Granny's *always* going on about her past! And if he's forgotten it, it's important he should be reminded.'

Aunt Claire laid her hand on my forehead, as though I was hot with a fever.

'It's the present that matters most, isn't it? And that's quite enough about Ha, too. It's you we've got to worry about at the moment. And I think it's time to go to sleep now.'

She put another log on the fire, brought me a pillow, and two blankets and tucked them round me as though I was a little baby.

'I hope you won't be too cold down here. I'll leave the stair light on so if you need anything, you only have to shout. If you get frightened or anything.'

'Thanks, but I'm never afraid in the night,' I said. What a stupid, arrogant thing to say. 'But I think Ha sometimes is. Do you know, he rocks all night?'

'He rocks? What's that?'

'Sort of shaking. Tony says it's what monkeys do in laboratories if you take them away from their mothers.'

'Well you won't have any rocking tonight.'

She didn't actually kiss me but said good-night in a very

friendly way.

With the light from the wood-fire flickering on the walls, I felt very secure in her house. The swimming in my head had stopped at last, and I was warm and comfortable against the cushions.

I knew now what I had to do. I had to go back home, though not to get rid of him, but to save him. In the morning I was going to rescue Ha, free him from the prison of his stupidity, restore to him his forgotten past. I could do it because deep inside, niggling me like a skinmite, a blowfly, a zigger caught in the sole of the foot, I knew that I knew things about him, things that weren't even in the reports. I didn't know how I knew, or why. I just did.

I woke with a raging thirst longing for cold water. Even thinking about the colour of the cocktail I'd mixed, made me feel sick. I found my way to the kitchen sink and drank from the tap. Their kitchen floor was tiled in black and white squares which I could just see in the dim light. But looking at them was strange, and made me feel frightened. I remembered the black and white draughts-board at home and the way Ha had stared at it. I remembered the black and white tiled floor in the photo in the beige file and the way the orphaned children were floundering on it like starved fledglings.

I fumbled my way back to the sofa but after that I didn't sleep so well. The baby coughed and cried, and nobody went to him.

Towards dawn the other children started crying, and that set them all off. How could I sleep when thirty abandoned orphans were whimpering in their cots all around me, when my skin itched all over, and when the warm air was so humid I could hardly breathe?

So I swayed myself in my cot from side to side and screamed in the back of my throat, because that was the way which blocked out all sensation. But then the woman came and slapped me and told me to stop it because it upset the others in the room. I thought she was my mother. But when I saw her face close to, I couldn't recognize her.

'It's not my fault!' I cried. But she didn't understand and she didn't say anything, she just picked me up quite roughly, and carried me along the stone balcony, down the stone steps to the washroom at the end. She stood me in the high sink and squirted cold water over my legs and bottom. Then, without drying me, she carried me back and replaced me in the cot.

I stared up at two mosquitoes which sat quivering on a ceiling fan which never moved and I wished I could remember who I was. When I heard gunfire in the distance and the wailing of a siren, I thought I half-remembered.

PART TWO
Ha

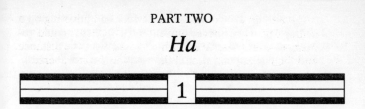

Our village lay inside a small loop of the river, and was rich, fertile land. The soil was dark-red so that, during the dry season, red dust clung to the grass and the leaves, and the air was close and still. But after the rainy season, everything grew new and green.

Beside the river we had rice paddies, and on the higher land we had fruit orchards and vegetable plots where we grew mangoes, bread-fruit, grapefruit and pineapples. Beyond the village we had plantations of bananas, and groves of bamboo. And beyond the bamboo came the forest.

Some families kept water-buffalo who did the work for them. In my family, we had a cow for milk, some hens and a goat. We harvested enough rice and vegetables for our family and the rest my mother sent downriver to market in the city. But we had to keep some rice back to pay our taxes to the men from the North, and a few vegetables to give as presents to the men from the South.

The men from the South usually came with the foreigners. The foreigners looked different from us. Their skin was pale and their forearms hairy. We children used to call them the round-eyes, though their eyes weren't really round.

Our village was large enough to have its own bicycle repair shop, and a school. But we had no teacher because Tran Van K'Xung had gone away to the South to be retrained.

Apart from bicycles we had no mechanical forms of transport. But alongside the track leading into the village there were three large vehicles, tipped sideways in the ditch, abandoned long ago by the men from the South. We used to climb on them, and pretend to drive them.

One night, some men from the North came. We watched them dismantle the parts and take them away in sacks on their backs. After they'd gone, we copied what they'd done. We had the rest of the parts ready, sorted into sizes and shapes, next time they came.

Then the disabled hulks of machine rotted into the landscape. Like the foliage of the forest, they too were soon covered in red dust, and then washed clean by the rains. They sank deeper into the earth. Bamboo and grass grew up round them and hid them. The metal began to rust, and we children didn't play on them any more. The paths around had been mined, and one girl was blown up. Our mothers didn't like us going there any more.

The men from the North came again and held an open meeting one evening in the disused school-hut. We all went, including the old people and the little children. The leader explained that they were members of the People's Army. Some of them wore uniform, like soldiers, or parts of uniform, but most of them looked like ordinary country people.

'The great machines you gave us,' said the leader, 'were M-113 armoured personnel carriers and we'd like to thank you for your help in dismantling them for us.' He explained that the round-eyes who'd left them in the ditch were foreign imperialists, aided by treacherous Government troops from the South who, like puppets on strings, would do whatever they were told, even if it meant fighting against their own people.

'So if we are to win the battle against Imperialism we must ask for your further co-operation and solidarity. And in return we'll protect you and support you.'

With the help of our village headman, they set up clubs. I was too young for Youth Liberation, but my mother was enrolled with the Women's Liberation, and my father joined the Farmer's Liberation. Even my grandmother was allowed to join the Veteran Women's Association because, when she was younger, she had worked with the president's illiteracy campaign. Now, she was allowed to help by sharpening bamboo spikes for *punji* traps in the forest. She sat up at night, chewing betel nuts to keep herself awake as she fulfilled her allocation, and by day she kept them in the straw underneath our cow.

Soon after the lecture in the school-hut, the harvest tax was raised again, to ten per cent per household, assessed on how much each family had produced, and my father had to pay two piastres a month to the Farmer's Liberation Association.

They told people what to do if the Government puppet troops and the foreign aggressors came again.

'They think that your village is in their control. In fact, it is in yours. People may come here from the city, and they'll have no idea that they're in one of the new liberated areas, so don't bother

64

to explain it to them. Don't arouse their suspicions.'

We had always been wary of strangers. Visitors always used to be taken first to the headman. But now we were told not to do this any more.

'Never question, or ask to see their ID papers, or it'll arouse suspicions, unless you've been warned by us in advance that they may be agents. Our territory, and the enemy's territory, is very closely interlocked, and you have the good fortune, and the honour, of being positioned on the borders, which is why you can be so much help to us. And to yourselves.'

When Tran Van K'Xung had been our teacher, only children went to school. But now, anybody who wanted could come along. They didn't only tell us about war and the enemy. They had other classes in the school-hut too. My mother rested in the evening because she was expecting a child. But my grandmother often went, especially when there were recitations of poetry. Her lips would move silently, as she followed word for word, long love poems about men and women meeting secretly, in sweet-scented pagoda gardens, beside misty lakes.

'I am like a piece of peach-coloured silk' — I saw her mouth forming the words almost before our new teacher could say them. *'Waving in the market-place, not knowing into whose hands I will fall.'*

I could hardly imagine bent old Grandma, with her stained, red teeth, as a silky-skinned young girl in love.

'Our melodious language,' the teacher told us, 'has been used since the time of Han Thuyen as the means of poetic expression. It is the language, too, of scholars, of tellers of folk-tales, of the nobility and of the mandarins. Yet, in their many attempts at national expression, colonialist invaders from China, France, America, have suggested that it's merely the crude, unformed language of the masses. And there's a danger that we may allow the purity of our mother tongue to be defiled by the infiltration of vocabulary from the imperialist regime. We must do all we can to guard against this. If we allow the enemy to invade our speech, this is only the first step to allowing him to invade our thoughts, crush our homes, and finally erode our whole way of life.'

I wasn't sure I believed what he said. Or perhaps I didn't understand what he meant. Apart from that one day when the land-mine had accidentally blown up near the abandoned trucks, our village had always been happy and peaceful. And I couldn't imagine anybody wanting to invade our thoughts and

65

homes. But I liked the way our new teacher spoke to us. I liked hearing him talking about our noble country, about the triumphs of the August Revolution, and our indomitable spirit, our right to struggle for freedom. He brought his rifle with him to the school-hut, propping it up in the corner, and afterwards he'd sometimes show us how it worked.

'The mother tongue is common to men from both the North and the South. It is the symbol of our struggle for national unity.'

Once the poetry was over, my grandmother lost interest. Out of the corner of my eye, I saw that she was already nodding off. But I wanted to keep awake because after the lecture, the teacher played his guitar, and we usually finished up with a noisy singing session. But he hadn't got to the end yet.

'During the previous occupation of our country by the French, the administration prevented students from studying in their mother tongue, on the pretext that our language was inappropriate for conveying complex scientific information. So all the schoolchildren took a secret pledge never to allow themselves to use any words of the colonial language, even in conversation with one another.'

My father had grown up under French rule. I wondered if he'd taken that pledge.

'So today, all you children can do the same. Try to avoid using any foreign words, whether of Chinese, or French, or American origin.'

But he didn't tell us how we were to know which of the words that we used *were* foreign.

'Nor does it owe its value,' he went on, moving to start another topic which might last for an hour, 'exclusively to its musical tone. Our balanced and harmonious language has a flexible syntax, varied system of vowels and consonants, and is rich with accents. Positive and negative horizontals, and four verticals, giving it a wide phonetic scale —'

I really didn't understand what he was talking about. Like my grandmother beside me, I felt very sleepy. I kept pinching my leg to make myself stay awake.

'Any further questions?'
    'Yes, sir, please, sir.'
    'Somebody speak?'
    'Me, sir.' It was Bodger. He had adenoids. He never worked, but liked asking silly questions to get attention.

'Got a question, sir. Why do we *need* to learn French, sir?'

'Sit down, Bodger. I said any serious questions? Anything you didn't understand about the use of *é* and *è* for example?'

'But, sir, it *is* a serious question.' We all knew perfectly well that it couldn't be. It was just that Bodger liked asking questions, any questions. Anything to hold up the lesson.

'All right, Bodger, what is it?'

'Well, sir, what I wanted to know, sir, is what do we learn French *for*, sir? What can we do with it?'

'You can sit your O levels with it, Bodger. And if only you had been fortunate enough to have been born with more sensitivity, you could have read the immortal lines of Baudelaire.'

'Yes, sir. Thank you, sir.'

I woke with a jolt when the singing and rhythmic clapping began. It was a new song about how our triumphant fight against illiteracy, against foreign feudalism, against famine, was leading us towards freedom from oppression.

My grandmother didn't join in. It was too noisy. She preferred quieter, more old-fashioned things. Sometimes she used to describe for me the most beautiful and peaceful spot in the whole world. The nearest place on earth to heaven, she said, were the gardens and the seven-tiered pagoda at Linh Mu with the gilded statue of the laughing Buddha on the veranda. Long ago, an elderly goddess appeared there, recognized the serenity of the place, and chose it as the site for the capital city for the people.

'And so, in the year sixteen hundred and one, the governor of Thuan Hoa planned and built the most beautiful pagoda of all time. And when I was young, I travelled to the Imperial City of Hué and visited Linh Mu and saw for myself.'

When my grandmother wasn't listening, my mother told me that grandmother hadn't really travelled. She'd only heard others describing their own pilgrimages and so had gradually come to believe that she'd been herself. I preferred to believe what my grandmother said because when she talked about the gardens strewn with petals, the brilliant scarlet poppies, the still air, I too could see it all quite clearly.

After the singing in the school was over, my grandmother and I walked home together, hand in hand. Moonlight was shining on the flooded paddies so that they were like silver, and it was on her face so that it looked as though it was made of silver too. Her shadow on the ground was dark blue.

'The wind pursues the moon from the sea to the mountains.'
She started reciting poetry, not silently, but aloud so I could see her. She did it better than the lecturer from the People's Army. *'With the wind, sadness spreads its quivering waves. My soul is sad like the seas, leave me not alone to meet my soul.'*

She wasn't really sad, but she liked sad poems.

The next day the men from the South arrived again. They didn't come quietly at night but very noisily in trucks. They didn't ask to see the village headman, they didn't do anything. They just drove into the village, and wandered about, though some of the children received sweets and soap.

Before the People's Army could return, the men from the South were back again. This time, they arrived with a lot of equipment. The Government puppet troops came in first. The round-eyed foreigners only came after the puppet troops had got us organized as they wanted us.

'Hello! Hello! This is Tran Van K'Xung, your teacher, returning home again!' They had a loudspeaker attached to one of the trucks which was so loud that we could hear his voice even down by the river. 'The Government has trained me to be a better teacher so our village will progress through education. These people are all your friends. Our own Republican soldiers and our American allies. They've all come to help you. They've come here today to give you a Hamlet Festival. There'll be music and good food. You will all come to the festival.' The truck, with Tran Van K'Xung's voice coming from it, drove slowly through the village.

'Hello! Hello! This is Tran Van K'Xung, your teacher, returning home!'

2

We always had good festivals in our village. The children's Lantern Festival when we visited each other's homes at dusk with our lighted paper lanterns shaped like birds, and the Shadow Festival, and the Feast of the Hungry Spirits. And in springtime, before rice-planting began, we had a Rice Festival with rockets and fireworks down on the banks of the river to bring a good crop to our fields. But this festival was different. We were ordered to go to it, yet we didn't prepare it ourselves. The soldiers prepared it for us.

They set up a small, brown hospital tent, with open sides, and Tran Van K'Xung's voice told us through the loudspeaker that there was free treatment for any child with skin disorders or worms.

And then, in another, larger tent, they offered us food. It was mostly their kind of food, patties of cooked meat, with bread. Some of the younger children went in to get the brightly-coloured fruit drinks, yellow and orange and pink. It looked like poison, and we had been warned by the men from the People's Front that the foreign invaders might try to poison the food they offered us.

And all day, music played loudly through the loudspeakers, and they tried to get the girls to dance. But they wouldn't.

And while the food was being given out, the soldiers selected some of the farmers and took them into a different tent, one at a time, and after an interval, let them out again.

My father was among those selected, and my mother was anxious. But when he came out, he merely shrugged and smiled.

'Just questions,' he said. 'They want me to join their army. But I'm a farmer, not a soldier.'

In the evening, they took down the tent, packed everything back on the trucks and drove away.

Two nights later the men from the People's Army came back, asking for active volunteers to help carry rice and supplies through the forests, to build blockades at other villages, to make roads impassable, to dig trenches, and set mines. My father volunteered. He never talked about what he did except to tell me that if I came across three small crossed sticks on a path I must not go on.

'Go back or go round another way,' he said. 'Never ever go on.'

The sticks were a sign meaning that the path ahead was mined, or booby-trapped.

Ha, d'you remember the war? Listen to me, Ha. I'm talking to you. This is terribly important. You were actually there. I've only got to try and imagine it and I can't if you won't co-operate. D'you remember what it was really like, being in a war? What happens?

Oh, you're so infuriating! Don't just stare at me like that. *Tell* me about it!

Then the Government puppet troops returned to organize another of their Hamlet Festivals, the same as the first with loud cheerful music, but this time without free food or medicine. The music played all day, and not Tran Van K'Xung, but an army officer, repeatedly told us we must co-operate with them. And while the music played, some of the soldiers who weren't trying to talk to the girls, searched through all the homes in the village. Whatever it was they were looking for they didn't find it that day, for towards evening they went away.

And so it went on. The Government puppet troops were fighting a war against communism, the People's Army were fighting against imperialism, and we were caught in the middle. By night we had to be with the men from the North, and by day with the men from the South.

My mother's baby was born and we called her Mai, and our neighbour's buffalo calved the same week. Then two teenage girls were billeted on us from Mi Hung which had been bombed. All their fields had been flattened, so they had no food. Nearly every home in our village had to take in somebody extra. The two girls and my mother didn't get on. The girls ate too much, and they wouldn't work hard enough, even though my mother shared everything very fairly with them.

She said they were greedy and lazy.

One of them cried a lot, and the other sat on a stool staring vacantly ahead as though seeing nothing. They walked slowly out to the fields and rested on their hoes half the time. When they fetched water, they only filled the bucket half full. The atmosphere at home grew tense. 'You rice guzzlers!' My mother shouted at them. 'You do nothing but eat!' I suppose I should have been sorry for them. It wasn't their fault they'd lost their

70

homes and had to come to us. But they were so sluggish and stupid all the time, I couldn't feel very sorry for them.

In the end, my mother went to the village headman and he agreed to have them billeted in another family, and the atmosphere was easier.

Mi Hung was a long way off. I'd never even heard of it until the people from there came to our village. But it was nearer than I had imagined. And what happened there, soon happened to us.

One day a small plane appeared, circling overhead, round and round like a bird spiralling on currents of warm air, and as it flew it rained pieces of paper into the village, hundreds and hundreds of leaflets which floated downwards, to land on the earth, on the thatched roof-tops, in the trees, in the hen-run. We all ran to pick them up. On one side, there was a drawing.

It showed a small man being blown up by shell-fire swooping across the picture from a long way off. Beside the little man was a picture of his home on fire, the grass roof burning in scarlet flames.

There was a message on the other side.

'Read it,' said my mother.

I read it to her and to our neighbour from next door.

> Artillery will soon hit your village. You must look for cover immediately. From now on, chase the enemy away from your village, so that the Government won't have to shell your area again.

'It's propaganda,' I said. The People's Army men had warned us about the imperialist propaganda.

At the bottom of the sheet was another message, printed in a different language. Although it was foreign, it was quite easy for me to read. The lecturer from the People's Army had warned us we weren't to let foreign languages invade and spoil the purity of our mother tongue. We were to avoid them, he'd said. But I wanted to know what it said, so I read it. But even though I could read the words, the information in them didn't make any sense to me. The message at the bottom just said:

Leaflet No: APC 6227. Army Psychological Warfare Unit.

Everybody looked curiously at the pictures on the leaflets but at first nobody believed that our village would really be bombed. The Government troops had said that they were our friends.

But the Mi Hung people said that they'd received just the same leaflets before a raid. So, with everybody else, we went straight out into the forest and waited there to see what would happen.

We heard the whine of fighter planes coming over. They flew backwards and forwards all day as warning. Then, at last, we felt the thumping of the ground as they started dropping shells.

There was a confusion of noises which felt as though they'd burst our ear-drums. The planes screamed through the sky, and the missiles fizzled like the bright fireworks at the Rice Festival. The baby screamed. And each explosion shook the forest, so you could feel the air moving and the leaves rustling.

Then, the bombing became less noisy. The explosions less frequent, fewer planes overhead. It was as though the attackers were exhausted by the raid. Then, finally it was all over. The raid had not lasted more than half an hour altogether, but we stayed hidden for a long time after we'd heard the bomber planes fly away.

When we came out, we saw that they'd missed the houses altogether. Instead, they'd left a trail of deep craters for a mile or more along the river bank, and the water, usually quite clear, mingled with the mud and flowed thick and dark.

The bombs had smashed into the rice paddies, bursting open the mud walls which separated the fields and held in the water, so that the growing crops were washed away by the red river water.

The paddies supplied our rice, our food, everything. There'd be a small harvest this year, and so our ten per cent tax to the People's Army would be smaller too.

Everybody had to work repairing the paddy walls. But it was harder than usual, for there were fewer men to help. My father said it was no longer safe for him to stay in the village. He went away and lived in the forest. My mother took him food every night.

The men from the People's Army knew that our village would be shelled again soon, and so they came back and showed us how to dig bomb-shelters underneath our homes. We built shelters for our livestock too, and each night we led our cow from her stall out to her own trench in the yard. It was just deep enough for her to stand in with only her head above ground, looking out.

Although we no longer had to run for the forest when we heard the planes coming, but could take cover beneath our own homes, the uncertainty of wondering when the next raid would come, and the noise when it did, was tiring.

The raids were early in the morning, just before daylight. By sunrise, when the mist was gathering over the river, the planes would be gone, having spattered our vegetable fields with craters of all different sizes.

Then, they began a new leaflet raid. This time, the pictures showed a man from the People's Army dying, with his face down in the dirt, with his hands clutching at the air in front of him, with jet planes raining black bombs on to him.

I read the message to my mother:

> Each day, each week, each month, more and more of your comrades, base camps and tunnels are found and destroyed. You are shelled more often, you are bombed more often. You are forced to move very often; you are forced to dig deeper, you are forced to carry more loads away. You are tired, you are sick. Your leaders tell you victory is near. They are wrong. Only DEATH is near. Do you hear planes? Do you hear bombs? They are the sounds of DEATH. Rally now to survive.

And again, at the bottom, in the foreign language, it said:
Leaflet No: AVIB 246, Army Psychological Warfare Unit.

'Read it again!' said my mother, so I read the leaflet aloud a second time while she stared at the picture of the man being bombed. But my grandmother took no notice at all. She merely spat a stream of betel-red juice into the dust and went on tapering her allocation of bamboo sticks to a fine spear-like point. When a week's supply was ready she gave them to me, and I carried them to the forest, and left them in a hole under the ferns. I never knew who came to collect them. I liked to think that it was my father.

After *Leaflet No: AVIB 246* the bombing got worse. It went on, with only short breaks, not just along the river banks and by the vegetable fields, but all through the forests around. We huddled in our shelter all the time.

Then, at dawn on the fourth day, I woke to a strange, unreal noise. It was a cock crowing against silence. The bombing was over.

We crept out from the shelter cautiously at first. We let out the hens, the goat, the cow. The cow was moaning, and blinking in the light. We fed the animals, and then my mother said she would prepare us a meal because we'd only eaten cold rice for three days. But first, we had to set about clearing up.

We always had to clear up after a bombing raid. The raids

created dust like in the dry season, only more. There was a powdering of red over everything inside our house — the bedding, the cooking pots, the walls, the corner shrine.

But we heard aircraft overhead again. It was a different noise from bombers, a whirring, flapping sound.

A helicopter appeared above the tree-tops of the forest with two speakers mounted on either side, which squarked out like an angry hen.

'Attention people of this village!' it squarked. It hovered overhead. 'You are surrounded by Republic and allied forces. Stay where you are and await instructions. Do not run away or you will be shot!'

More helicopters came bobbing over the tree-tops, growing larger and filling the bright, white sky. We didn't run for cover, but stood in front of our home, open-mouthed, craning our heads back, staring up at the huge, black shapes against the sun. They weren't like the bomber planes which skimmed like knives through the air. They seemed rather to lurch like heavy flappy birds.

As they began their descent towards us, we could see that each had automatic weapons mounted on the sides, and that each flew with the side doors open, with armed men perched right near the opening, khaki legs hanging over the edge into space. I could see the undersides of their leather boots, the under rims of their metal helmets like a dark aura round each head.

The noise was fearful. The rotating wings blew up dust, and blasted hot air down into our faces. It made me feel nauseous looking up at them as they pitched from side to side through the air, and I knew I'd seen it all before, just the same as now. I'd never left the village. I'd never flown in one of those things, but I knew that this moment had already happened before.

Our French teacher once talked to us about *déjà vu*. He told us that the sense of being somewhere you've never seen before, yet feeling that you know it already, was perfectly normal and quite common.

'*Déjà vu*, the illusory sense of having already experienced a present situation. Curiously, though this psychological phenomenon is doubtless common to many nations, we have no expression for it in our own language. So we turn to the French and take *déjà*, meaning already. And *vu*, meaning seen. Thus conveying the sense of an

74

"already seen" situation.'

He went on to tell us of other French phrases which have been absorbed into our everyday language — *rendezvous, tour de force, bloc, bulletin,* and *finesse.* They didn't sound like the sort of words we'd miss if we hadn't got them.

'But why, sir?' It was Bodger.

'Why what?'

'Why do the French want other countries to use their words for things when we've got a jolly good language of our own?'

We watched the helicopters circle, then bump down, one after another in rapid succession, on to our vegetable gardens. The men jumped out and ran, bent double as though themselves afraid of being fired on, over melons, beans, celery, trampling with their boots on whatever produce hadn't already been destroyed by shells.

This time there was no pretence at having Hamlet Festivals. They were disciplined and determined. There were none of the Government puppet troops in the first wave. They were all the foreign round-eyes. They were fanning out, to encircle our village.

'We must go in,' said my mother, and she hurried us inside.

But my grandmother was in a trance, dazed by three nights in the shelter. My mother sat her down gently on the stool and gave her the baby to hold while she saw to the clearing up.

The room was suddenly darkened by a huge man, higher than the door lintel, blocking out the light. He was so tall that he had to stoop to stand in the doorway, and even then the top of his helmet was lost in the grass-thatch.

'Where's your husband, lady?' he shouted.

His skin was as dark as ripe figs, his nostrils wide open like a boar's snout, his eyes bulbous and red-rimmed. He held an automatic low at his hip and pointed it first at my grandmother with the baby, then at my mother.

My mother snatched the baby back from my grandmother and held it to her tightly. The huge dark man instinctively twitched his gun back at her. He was very frightened.

'Your husband! Where is he?'

He didn't see me. I was in the folds of my father's jacket hanging on a peg. But as I flattened myself more against the wall I knocked an earthenware dish down from the shelf. It clattered to the floor.

The jumpy black man shot over our heads into the roof and one of the hens, roosting in the thatch, caught the hail of fire and flopped down to the ground, dead but still squarking. The man swung round and fired into the garden, then swung back to us, and took a step hesitantly into the house, gesturing with his gun.

'Where's your husband?' he shouted.

She didn't understand. He shouted it again. I knew what he was saying. The People's Army had told us not to spoil our mother tongue with foreign languages, but how could I help it if I understood everything they said?

She stared at him, not insolent, not stupid, just stared.

Without moving further into the room, he looked carefully round. It was quite small. There was nowhere for a man to be hiding. My parents' cane bed on one side, the baby's basket, my bedroll. Our possessions hanging from pegs on the walls. We cook in another room with open sides. The soldier saw the wicker basket full of our clothes, all dusted in red.

He began to poke into it with the point of his gun.

'Clothes!' my mother said. But he didn't understand her any more than she understood him. Although I could understand both, I didn't know how to explain his words to her.

She took out the dusty red garments, one by one, and the soldier watched carefully, then nodded.

'OK, I get the message. That's your laundry bin. Now where's your husband!'

My mother remained standing where she was. He had the gun. She had the baby. I could see her growing angry, but outwardly she looked calm. She was very beautiful. 'I don't understand why you round-eyes keep on coming here,' she said quietly. 'Why can't you go away? You know, we're fed up with you round here.'

'All I have to know,' the black man yelled, 'is where is your husband?'

'You drop messages on us, you bomb the paddies,' my mother went on grumbling. 'You kill our livestock. What else do you want?'

The soldier seemed to despair of getting through to her.

He called out to another soldier who was searching through the hen-coops.

'What do I do with her?'

'Any weapons? She look suspect?'

'No, just a very pretty stack of woman, with an old crone, and a couple of kids.'

'Leave her.'

'OK, lady, you stay right here.' He turned and went away.

A minute later he was back with three others.

'You numbskull! You don't send them back into their homes. You round them up!'

So we were ordered out of the house, two soldiers behind us, one at the side, the leader shouting at them, telling them what to do. They all did a lot of shouting. We were silent.

'Your job's to keep anyone from escaping, right? Block off that path. No way through. If it's just a bunch of women and kids wandering about and don't know what's happening, don't fire. Just bring them in as best you can. But otherwise, you got to take them under fire. Anything that moves out there, that's VC. Got it?'

They used the loudspeakers attached to the first helicopter, to warn us we must move quickly to the centre of the village, otherwise we'd be shot as VC suspects.

I didn't know what VC was.

'It's their term,' said my mother. 'It means nothing to us. There's no VC, so none of us can be VC.'

But it did mean something to them. It was their word for any person who was with the People's Army or who knew anything about the People's Army, who had ever done anything for the People's Army. In their language, a VC suspect was any person who owned a pair of shoes, any person who owned a shirt with buttons, any person not carrying an Identification Card, any person who didn't wear a straw sun-hat.

We were led, or shoved, or driven like a herd of buffaloes towards the school-hut.

'You have no father,' my mother said as we hurried along. 'If anybody questions you, remember he went away a long time ago. No father. Don't forget.'

My grandmother shuffled and muttered irritably. But some of the little children went skipping along as though expecting a festival with pink drinks.

I knew something terrible was going to happen, worse than being in an air-raid for three days. Everything was going to change. We should turn and run while we had the chance, and hide in the green. But my mother didn't understand. She didn't hear the things the foreign soldiers said to one another. Only I

77

understood and it was too difficult to explain. I only knew that somehow, I had allowed the melodious purity of the mother tongue to be infiltrated by the language of the colonial aggressors.

The soldiers had seemed so big and menacing when they streamed out of their helicopters. Now, closer to, they were young and jittery, and uncertain what they were to do. They were rough with us.

'What we gonna do with all these people?'

'Interrogation first. In the school house.'

'What after?'

'Resettlement. A good temporary camp.'

'Prisoner of War? But they aren't P.O.W.'s. We just taken them out of their homes. They're civilians.'

'Hostile civilians. We've orders to clear this village, spring-cleaning. While we're doing that, they'll be safer in camp.'

'It doesn't seem right, somehow, moving them out when they've not done anything.'

'They'll be quite happy there. All amenities.'

We were assembled in the shade of the school house, everybody of the village who could be found. Then, we saw a solitary figure moving slowly away down the main street. It was old Giau Huc, on his bicycle, pedalling towards his vegetable garden, his straw hat tipped to the back of his head, his hoe and basket strapped to his bicycle carrier. He was deaf from an explosion. He was also obstinate, and a bit stupid. He couldn't hear the loudspeakers. All the villagers' eyes were on him. One of the soldiers spotted him. He shouted after him. Giau Huc couldn't hear the shout. He pedalled on. We watched the distant figure, his round, yellow hat bright against the dark trees, and we all knew what was going to happen and we were unable to do anything about it. I seemed to see it all happen long before it really did, the slow flying fall of Giau Huc, gracefully sideways, with the sound coming after.

The soldier called after him again.

'Git back here! Do you hear me! Git on back here with the others! That's orders!'

Another soldier, very young, with a red face, and pale hair, raised his weapon.

Giau Huc's pedalling feet went on, round and round.

The young soldier fired, and a moment later, there were more bursts of machine-gun fire from another group of soldiers who'd also seen Giau Huc going the wrong way. Giau Huc seemed to move up in the air as though flying, in a slow spray of dust and movement, away above his bike, and then gently sideways and down into the rain-water ditch beside the path.

The young red-faced soldier ran cautiously towards the body, half crouching, as though afraid it might get up and fire back. When he saw there was no movement, he straightened up and stared at it for several moments as his friends gathered round.

'He's dead. Yep,' one of them said.

'That's a VC for you,' said another. 'He's a VC all right.'

'That's what they wear, them black pyjamas. That's their uniform, ain't it? He wouldn't wear that if he was a genuine farmer. It wouldn't make sense, on account of black absorbs heat. It's a hot country, you don't wear black clothing out in the meadow, get too damned hot.'

'No, that can't be right, sir. That's no uniform. They all wear them black pyjamas, and the white shirt. All the people. Haven't you seen them back in town, all wearing that?'

'Sure they all wear it. They're all VC. Didn't you hear the captain telling us at the briefing? Solid VC country here, as long as anyone can remember, that's what he said. And look at his feet.'

Giau Huc had bare feet, brown.

'See! All muddy from burrowing down them holes they dig everywhere for living in. They're more like coneys than humans.'

'I don't think he was no VC. He don't have no weapon.'

The hoe lay on the ground beside Giau Huc. One of the soldiers kicked it with his toe-cap. 'What's that then, if it isn't a weapon? Of course he was VC. You saw him, moving away when he was told to stop. If he'd stopped when we told him to stop, he wouldn't have got shot, would he?'

'That's right.'

'Lieutenant told us we were to shoot if they move. But no women and kids.'

The red-faced man who'd fired the first shot at Giau Huc, bent over and peered closely into Giau Huc's face.

'I shot him!' he said. It was the first thing he'd said. 'That's the first time I ever killed anybody before!' He seemed surprised but not upset.

One of them had a black camera on a strap round his neck and he began to take photographs of the body.

A few of the soldiers tried to be playful and friendly. They offered candybars to the smaller children, they tried to smile and chat to the girls. With elaborate gestures, they tried to find out their names, and explain their own. But we'd all seen Giau Huc shot. These men were as unlike human beings as the helicopters they had arrived in. They were like flying snakes, dangerous and unreliable.

They were larger than us, and armed and hairy. There was nothing to be done except obey their orders but not communicate. People's faces were closing off. They might have been dreaming with their eyes open, like the dead. Even the little children soon copied the mood of their parents, and sat still and silent.

The questioning went on all morning. It was hot and sultry. The sun rose higher and the air became drier.

Several long rattles of machine-gun fire sounded across the village near where Giau Huc had fallen. A man was firing random bursts into an outhouse. It was the same one who'd shot Giau Huc. Another soldier shouted angrily at him.

'Come back here! Stop that fooling around!'

But the red-faced boy went on shooting into the out-house and into the yard beside it and into the trees until his target, a buffalo tethered to a post in a yard, finally sank to its knees, and rolled over on to its side with a groan.

'You're not to kill buffalo!'

The soldier-boy ambled back to the schoolhouse, grinning.

3

'What was he doing?'

'He says he doesn't remember what he was doing.'

'Does he pay taxes?'

'Yes. The men from the North come and collect two piastres a month.'

'What's his job?'

'He says he's a farmer.'

'Let's see his hands. Show me. He's no farmer! His palms are smooth, not hard and calloused. Ask him what he does.'

'He says he's been repairing bicycles for other people.'

'Why did he say he was a farmer then?'

'He says, he used to be a farmer, until Ben Rach was evacuated and then he came to live here with these people. He's been helping.'

'How has he been helping?'

'With the harvest, he says. But now he repairs bicycles.'

The questioning was less casual than the time before when they questioned my father. They sorted us into groups. The older boys and men were put on one side of the schoolyard, the women and children the other. I was with the women and children.

Each person was led, one by one, into a brown tent, while the rest stayed outside, sitting in the shade, watched over by the soldiers. Nobody talked. Nobody moved, they just listened to the endless murmuring of the interrogators' voices inside the tent.

My mother, with the baby resting on one arm, sat perfectly still, straight-backed, not looking at anybody, only staring ahead, her smooth face a blank. She moved only once, to nurse my sister.

At last, it was her turn. I got up to go with her.

'Not you, Sonny Jim,' said the soldier, and pushed me back from the open tent flap. I was afraid of what would happen to her in there, but instead of looking frightened, she merely looked annoyed and glared angrily at the soldier who led her in. I sat down outside the tent and strained hard to hear.

The questioning was done by an American captain, with a Government soldier as interpreter.

'Has she ever seen VC?' said the captain. He spoke in a loud, flat voice.

'Have you ever seen VC?' said the interpreter. His voice was softer and quieter, rising and falling. My mother's voice was the quietest of all so that I could hardly hear.

'Yes, sometimes. Everybody knows they're about. But nobody knows who they are.'

'Yes, she says sometimes, of course,' said the interpreter.

'Where does she see them?'

'Where do you see them?'

'Out walking in the fields, many weeks ago,' said my mother.

'Where were they going?'

'She says she doesn't know. It's not her business to know about things like that. She says she lives in the village and looks after her old mother and her children. She says she doesn't go following strangers into the forest.'

'What were the VC doing in the fields?'

'How should I know?'

'She says she doesn't know. It's not her business.'

'Where's her husband?'

'Where's your husband?'

Perhaps the foreign captain should have asked different questions. Have you seen your husband lately? What were you doing last week at dawn before it was light? Why did you take a small bowl of rice and a parcel of cooked vegetables wrapped up in leaves into the forest? Why did you walk quietly without a lamp, and leave your baby behind in the house?

But he didn't ask questions like that. He asked, with boredom, the same questions he asked everybody. And she gave the same answers.

'She says she doesn't know. He went away a long time ago, and it's been very hard. He might be dead for all she knows. There's been bombing. Mi Hung was flattened by raids. All the people had to come here to their village.'

'Is her husband VC?'

'She says, No, he isn't. She says she doesn't think anybody in this village is.'

'Well *somebody* must be!' said the captain. 'What's going on in this place? Every peasant we question has never known anybody who's VC, has never seen any VC close up. Don't they know there's a war going on all round them? How can we fight a war if we never make contact with an enemy? When we don't even know who the enemy is, let alone where?'

Instead of waiting for the next question my mother began to complain in a high, whining voice about what had happened in our village that morning.

'One of your soldiers, a great dark man, shot one of my hens roosting in the roof,' she said to the interpreter. 'Go on, tell him,' said my mother. 'You have to repeat what I say.'

'She says that this morning a soldier from your army shot one of her hens.'

'A good laying hen,' added my mother.

'A good layer,' said the interpreter.

'Who's going to pay for my hen?'

'Listen, woman, oh, tell her, we're fighting a war here. We're trying to liberate her country, not playing farmers. What's one hen compared to the loss of 12,000 young men? No, don't say that. She won't understand what I mean.'

My mother began to describe all the special things about the hen.

'Will you tell her to kindly answer the questions as they're put to her,' snapped the captain. 'Tell her she'll get compensation if she applies to the right source. God almighty, one laying hen! But she's quite right though. We've got to play down this shooting at the peasants' livestock, or we'll have H.Q. down on us like a ton of bricks. How do we expect these villagers to trust us if the troops go round letting fire at everything that moves? And as for that buffalo the morning, that'll cost us a few bucks. What's a buffalo worth these days?'

'Ten dollars, sir, or four hundred piastres. But it belonged to the VC suspect Private Armstrong shot on the bicycle. So maybe it won't cost us anything.'

My mother seemed to have decided she had answered enough questions. She went on and on about our cow. How the noise of the air raid would almost certainly dry up its milk. Then what would we do? How, moreover, could she answer questions in the middle of the afternoon, when she couldn't remember a thing because bombs were falling so loudly for the past three days. And if one hen could be shot while she was right there in her house, what might happen when she was not at home? Why wasn't she allowed to bring the rest of her livestock into the schoolyard with her, to keep it safe? By the time she returned home, she might find the whole lot had been shot at by the soldiers.

The interpreter, struggling to interpret my mother's quiet but unceasing complaints, said to the officer, 'This woman is very angry, sir. And very worried about her animals.'

The officer scratched his head. 'All right, let her go. Bring in the next.'

My mother came out of the tent, her back straight, her head up. She hitched the baby on to her hip and walked serenely, gracefully back to her place in the yard. She did not look into the eyes of anybody, not even me. But though her face was empty, I felt sure I could see a glow of triumph behind the sullen stare.

The soldiers made a pile of the things they'd found in a cache in the forest, and displayed them in front of us as evidence of the village's collective guilt. There were some rifles and grenades, some tin canteens, and several store-tins of rice.

'But that old man wasn't carrying a weapon, was he? We were told only shoot if they're carrying weapons. That's how you know they're the enemy.'

'Well, OK. So some people without weapons get killed. So what are we supposed to do about it? We spot a guy out there in black pyjamas. What do we do? Wait for him to pull his AK-4 on us? I tell you I'm not. I'm going to get through this alive and then get on home. You're just a crispy critter, aren't you? That's because you're new out here. How long since you been here? One week? Two weeks? This the first time you been in an action situation?'

'Yes.'

'This is the first time you seen men greased?'

'Yes.'

'You'll get to understand how it is out here in a while. Listen, son, how old are you?'

'Eighteen last week, sir. They made me stay on board till my birthday.'

'If you don't like fighting, you shoulda joined the Peace Corps. But if you want to survive, if you want to get on home and see your mom and pop, and if you want to eat blueberry pie again, momma's own filling, you are gonna have to learn fast. Be sharp. On guard. Or else, as soon as you think you're safe, zap, some gook's gonna get you first. In combat, you don't get to have no second chances. OK?'

'Yes.'

'So maybe I'm wrong, and that poor old boy we got this morning was innocent. Maybe he was just an old granpappy. And maybe again he was not. Sometimes they throw their weapons into the bushes, far away, just as they hear you coming.

You go and look at the body, and fifty yards away there's an automatic lying in the bushes. You can't always tell from a long way off if they're carrying a weapon, and you don't want to get too close to find out. Not if you want to get on home and enjoy a nice white Christmas next year.'

Some people came out of the interrogation tent with their arms tied behind their backs with twine, and a brown label on a string hanging round their necks. They weren't led back to their place, in the yard, but were taken over to the far corner.

A boy called Van Lan Long who was only three years older than me, was led out like that, with his arms tightly bound behind him, just above the elbow. He was barefoot and wearing only cotton shorts. The top of his head came up as far as the guard's ammunition belt.

'You mean this little kid's suspect?' one of the soldiers said.

'This kid, as you call him, has probably been gun-running for five years. A ten-year-old comes up, takes your candy, and next minute, wham, he drops his grenade! This innocent boy probably caused the death of a good many of your best buddies just like that. Anyhow, these gooks always look younger than they are. They're a stunted race.'

Van Lan Long was pushed roughly towards the far corner. As he stumbled past, I saw the brown card label they'd put round his neck. 'Captive Card', it said, printed in our language and theirs, and underneath there were spaces to put the person's name and age and work. They'd filled in his name but left the rest empty.

Altogether, they selected twenty people as captives, including our village headman, and they sat them in two rows, squatting, their hands behind their backs, with a guard at each end of each row. We tried not to look directly at them. They were all people we knew, and they didn't look across at our side of the yard. Even wives didn't look at husbands, or mothers at sons.

A large helicopter, bigger than the ones the army had come in, landed bumpily in the road outside the school. It had two sets of whirling blades, one at each end, which blasted up red dust into our faces. The guards hid their faces in their arms against the swirling dust, and so did we. But the captives, with their arms tied, could only close their eyes and let the hot dust blow at them.

The back end of the helicopter was lowered, to form a bridge leading up into the dark opening of the inside. The captives were ordered, with gestures, to crouch low to avoid being chopped up by the whirling blades, and to run towards the opening.

85

They ran in single file, up the gangway and into the darkness, with their brown labels flapping in the wind.

The gang-plank was drawn up so that we couldn't see them any more. The helicopter took off with more roaring and wind. Seventeen men and three boys from our village were lifted up, soaring above our heads into the sky, and disappeared away over the trees.

Four green, open-sided, military trucks rumbled into the centre of the village. They swung round, churning up the road, and parked in a straight line. Their drivers shouted and gestured, but nobody understood what they wanted. The people thought that the trucks had come to take the rest of the soldiers away.

I knew why they were there. I knew what the men were shouting.

'God Almighty! These people, they're so stupid! So obstinate!'

The interpreter was found. He explained that we were being taken to our resettlement camp. My grandmother could not believe that she was supposed to climb on board and leave.

She began to wail and shook her head from side to side. 'It's a mistake to move people off their hallowed land,' she moaned. 'It's a terrible mistake.'

One of the American soldiers patted her on the shoulder. 'Don't you worry about it Grandma. You'll love it!' he said.

But of course, she didn't understand what he said, any more than he understood the difficulty about leaving. When a person goes away from his place, he leaves a part of himself behind. My grandmother was afraid that if she left our home, it might be for ever, and then she would lose herself. Nor could she abandon the graves of our ancestors. If there was nobody to care for the tombs, the souls of her ancestors would be in eternal torment. The deceased cannot be forgotten, for their spirits affect the daily lives of their descendants.

Each household was allowed to bring fifteen bushels of rice and as much hand baggage as we could carry. I caught our six yellow chicks, and packed them into a wattle basket with the mother hen. She was a vicious creature and clucked angrily and tried to peck me, but finally, when the chicks were settled underneath her, she calmed down.

My mother packed the meal she had begun preparing, and our cooking pots, our sleeping mats, a basket of fresh vegetables, an earthenware jar of fish sauce, and a bundle of spices. On the window-ledge stood a row of sprouting bean seedlings, each growing in its little ball of damp earth, and wrapped around in green palm leaves. My mother had them ready to plant after the rains.

If she left them there till we came back, they'd probably die from lack of water. She packed them in a basket on top of some clothes.

My grandmother carried the baby, a tin bucket full of maize, and her own little wooden stool. Before we left the house, she placed a small offering of food and flowers in front of the household shrine in the corner and lit some sticks of incense and said some prayers in memory of all those who had passed on.

It was hard to carry so much. The five bags of rice were the heaviest, and though we tried, my mother and I could not move them. I had to ask one of the soldiers to help us, though my mother would rather I hadn't.

'We should've kept those lazy girls with us,' she muttered.

Our neighbours, who'd taken in the two evacuees, were able to bring more of their possessions with them since they now had more adults to help carry.

At the last minute, I thought to fill a small bag with some handfuls of grain so I'd have something to feed to the chicks as soon as we arrived.

At the trucks, several families had their pigs with them, squealing and struggling on the end of ropes tied to the back leg. We had no pig. And our cow was too large to bring, but we had the goat. I sprinted back to fetch her. She wouldn't run so I folded up her spindly legs like the legs of grandmother's stool and carried her in my arms.

A soldier stood at the tail-board, helping people up. He began to argue with a woman who had far more than her allocation of rice.

'Fifteen bushels only, madam! You heard.'

The woman tried to explain that her family was large, she had numerous extra relatives billeted on her when their village was evacuated, and how could she feed them for more than a minute on a mere fifteen bushels?

While they discussed it, I quickly scrambled up with the goat, and several others with excess baggage did the same.

The trucks moved off. The road was bumpy with pot-holes and craters where shells had missed the paddies. We were in convoy with two trucks behind and one ahead. We lurched and swayed with the movement of the vehicle. I was curious to see what lay beyond our village. I had often travelled in the forest near home, and when the men went fishing, I'd been downriver as far as the waterfall. But I'd never travelled this far along the road. I wondered if we would go as far as the city on the coast, where the river met the sea. I'd never seen the sea, nor had anybody from our village.

Some of the small children didn't realize at all what was happening and thought it was another Festival Day. They laughed and sang, and waved at the passing trees. Some of the very old, too, were so confused that they didn't realize either.

The convoy swung suddenly off the track, through a gate, and into a vast open space, like a field, cut out of the forest. At the further corner from the gate, up against the fence and in the full glare of the sun, with nothing to shade them, stood a neat row of brown tents. In that whole vast area surrounded by a high wire fence there grew no grass, or anything green except for three straggling palms. The ground was flattened red earth, covered over with red dust, nothing else.

'Here ya then, folks. Hotel Miami, your tropical holiday camp!' The driver unhooked the tail-board and indicated that we too were to get out. 'Home sweet home. We've arrived at your very own destination.'

Another soldier grinned, but none of our people did.

Tied to the gate was a cotton banner.

WELCOME TO THE RECEPTION CENTRE FOR THOSE WHO FLEE REPRESSION

We straggled, with our belongings, across the dry open space to the distant line of tents. They were of dark-brown fabric, with wooden poles, and set close to each other. There was the same sized tent for each family, however many or few there were in that family.

The trucks which had brought us turned to leave; a jeep swerved through the gates and bounced towards us across the huge expanse of flattened earth and pulled up directly in front of the row of tents in a swirl of dust. The officer in the back jumped quickly out, and climbed up on to the bonnet of his jeep, the better to be seen. He was small, wearing a very tidy, neatly-pressed uniform. He had a cone-shaped megaphone to talk through.

'Good day, my friends. I am Captain Nguyen Hué, your district chief of this relocation area. Welcome to your resettlement camp. Here, you'll be safe from attack by counter-insurgents. I regret that conditions may be difficult, just at first.

89

But please be patient. With our friends and allies from the foreign army, we'll do all we can, as quickly as we can, for your comfort. Water supplies, medical aid, and food will shortly be provided. Please remember to keep your ID cards with you at all times. Thank you for your co-operation.' Then he climbed down into the back of the jeep, sat down, and it bumped him back across the desolate field.

While my mother arranged things tidily inside the tent, I let out the fowl. The chicks ran with high-pitched peepings round and round in circles as though they'd lost all sense of direction during the truck ride. They pecked at the ground, and at my feet, and made little leaps up the sloping sides of the tent trying to fly away. I scattered some grain for them and they darted towards it, but the hen got there first, kicked her chicks out of the way and began greedily pecking it all up. I tried to spread it out so they'd all have some.

My mother put the bean seedlings outside the tent, along the side, where they would be shaded from the sun and where we wouldn't trip over them. My grandmother spread out our mats, and we lay down to sleep. It was lucky there were only four of us, because there was enough room for us all to spread out comfortably. The tent was wide enough for me to lie across the width of it, and the baby took up almost no space at all, for she lay with my mother in the curl of her arm. The people in the next tent had more trouble, because there were eleven of them and their pig.

I fell asleep almost at once and when I woke the place had changed. There was a lot of noise and activity going on. Trucks were roaring backwards and forwards, and soldiers were putting up more rows of tents just in front of our row. In front of some of the tents, small cooking fires glowed, where those lucky enough to have brought a supply of kerosene or charcoal, or to have gathered small pieces of kindling off the ground, were beginning to cook some rice for their evening meal.

I crawled to the back end of our tent and looked out under the flap to where the barbed wire fence was close enough for me to reach and touch. Beyond it, was tall, dry grass and scrubland and beyond that the beginning of the forest. Some more soldiers with knives were hacking back the scrub to make a wide path all round the camp, and then they were putting up a second line of wire fencing, even higher than the first.

The small officer in the crisp, neat uniform came round again and made another speech through his megaphone. Again, he clambered up on to the bonnet of the jeep so that we could all see and hear.

'Friends, I am Captain Nguyen Hué.' He always began like that. 'Your district chief of this relocation area. I am happy to be able to tell you that the water supply will shortly be made available and that many improvements are already under way. Please tell your friends and relations who may be out in the forest to give themselves up now, and there'll be less trouble for all of us. We, with our American allies, have installed you in this camp to save you from the terrors of the enemy. Those who don't give themselves up voluntarily, will certainly be killed by one side or the other. If your friends give themselves up and cease their futile struggle, they'll be saved.'

'How does he think we can get in touch with anybody,' my mother snarled, 'when we're shut up in a cage?'

It didn't seem like a cage. In the beginning there was always something interesting going on to watch, while the grown-ups were busy settling in.

First of all, the water supply arrived. It was a truck with a large, metal cylinder full of water mounted on the back. A soldier drove it a very short way into the compound and left it standing by the gates, half blocking the entrance. There was one tap at the back of the cylinder and almost before the driver had climbed down from the cab, a queue of people were lining up at the tap with buckets and tin mugs, basins, and old petrol cans. At first, everybody waited quietly, but as the crowd grew, people at the back got impatient and began to jostle. I ran back to our tent for a plastic can to fill up. The chicks, the hen, the goat, and the bean seedlings all needed water and so did we.

More tents went up, in identical rows, and more people arrived, as we had, in army trucks, with old people complaining, and babies crying and toddlers running away, and pigs squealing and hens clacking, till the whole place was packed tight with people and animals and looked quite different from the empty field when we'd first arrived. My mother spoke to a woman queueing at the water-tank who said that she and her family had already been relocated four times, and her youngest child had been born in camp.

As the camp grew it was no use Captain Nguyen Hué standing up on his jeep shouting at us through his megaphone. There were far too many people. So a tall wooden post was fixed up in the middle of the compound with a loudspeaker attached to the top and his speeches were relayed through that.

The loudspeaker announced that Revolutionary Development Department Workers were beginning an educational programme for us.

'You needn't go to it,' said my mother. 'They'll teach you all the wrong things.'

But you didn't have to go anywhere. It was broadcast non-stop through the relay system so that everybody had to listen even if they didn't want to. First, there was loud, cheerful music. Then a voice welcomed us on behalf of the Revolutionary Re-education Department, praised the work of the allied forces, and warned us of the dangers of enemy cadres which were being secretly set up in our midst.

'When you see a cadre forming, come immediately and tell us,' urged the voice of the Revolutionary Re-education Department. 'We also request all enemy cadres to turn themselves in, when they will be made welcome under our Open Arms programme. We advise all families with relations still missing, or hiding in their home villages, or in any other place, to come into the forest with the Government army and try to persuade their relatives to come back here to you. The Government will always stay with its people. The Government will always stay with its people. The Government will always stay.'

The loud cheerful music began blaring out again. And an hour later, the same speech was relayed all over again.

'I wish I was going deaf like Grandma,' said my mother.

They repeated the same message, and the same music, several times a day. At first, it was difficult not to listen to it, but gradually one grew used to it as background noise, and could think one's own thoughts, or even doze through it. But I was disappointed. I had expected lectures on poetry and language like we had had in the school-hut at home.

In between the message and the music, the education workers went round fixing up notices to the barbed wire, and even persuaded some of the smaller children to help them, but I knew my mother wouldn't like it if I helped. One of the notices, fixed to the fence just behind our tent, said, 'The Army Protects its People so that they can keep their rice and take it back to their villages.' As soon as it was put up, my mother tore it down.

The next thing to watch was the soldiers who came and started digging two long trenches, side by side, in the hard earth.

'What are they up to now?' my mother asked. My grandmother said it looked like graves to bury us in, and told the neighbours so. Because she was old, they believed her and passed it on to the people in the next tent.

My mother told me to go and find out what they were really doing, so I joined the straggle of children standing on the edge of one of the pits watching the men working. The holes went deeper and deeper, but they didn't seem wide enough for burying bodies. The soldiers fetched wooden stakes and sheets of corrugated iron from a truck and hammered the stakes into the ground and fixed up the sheeting like a low fence between the two pits.

We still couldn't think what they were for, until Captain Hué's voice, rising and falling like a strange dream-voice, announced that they were latrines, one for women and children, the other for men and boys. The metal fence was meant to separate them.

Another time, the entertainment was an American soldier driving his truck slowly up and down the rows, between the tents, while a Government soldier stood in the back working a pump which sprayed out a fine, white powder. It settled on everything like white dust, our bedding, our hair, our tents, even on our goat and the hens.

The paths between the rows of tents were narrow, and the truck was wide, so that the sides of the truck brushed against the canvas and sometimes pulled against the ropes. The huge wheels flattened the tent pegs down into the ground, and ran over people's baskets or their clothing put out to air, unless the owners were quick enough to rush out and move them.

The dust made our black hair change to grey so that we all looked like old people, even the baby, Mai. We didn't know why they wanted to blow dust all over us, and when the truck reached the next row we heard shouting and the truck engine stopped. I ran to see what was going on. The people in the next row were climbing up on to the truck and attacking both soldiers, the white and the brown one, with their hands. Then they pulled them down so they couldn't go on spraying. Some people in camp were always looking for an argument or something to shout about, because they just couldn't get used to having nothing to do all day, and no fields to have to work in from morning to night.

A woman screamed at me, 'Go and wash it off! Quickly! It'll

burn your skin off. Like poison!'

Another woman said that they'd had a yellow powder similar to this poured on to their village from a plane. All the leaves had withered and all the children had been burned. 'Go and tell your mother to wash you now. And throw away your food, or your insides'll be shrivelled up!'

The American driver shook his attackers off. 'You people are crazy!' he shouted at us in his own language. 'This isn't defoliant! It's disinfectant! Oh Jeeze, you people!' He turned to the soldier who'd been working the pump. 'Go and tell your people, bonzo boy, tell them they're crazy. Tell them it's *not* defoliant!'

But the American and the Government soldier didn't speak the same language so they didn't understand each other.

Government soldiers and the Americans were always having arguments and even when they did seem to understand what the other was saying, they pretended not to. But neither of these soldiers could pretend not to notice how angry everybody was about the powder, so they had to stop spraying.

I didn't really believe what the women were saying about the powder burning your skin. It wasn't hurting mine. But I did as they told me. I went to the water-tank by the entrance gates.

When I got there I found there was no water left for washing, or for anything else. A very small girl was splashing about under the tap. She had a plastic bucket with her and she was meant to be filling it for her family. Instead, she had left the tap on to make a pool in which she could play.

There was only a tiny dribble left, coming from the tap, but when I shouted at her for being so stupid, she just wandered off.

The ground round the water-tank was like a swamp, and as soon as some of the nearby people saw what had happened, they brought their pigs over to drink from the muddy puddles. The pigs were all right. But for the rest of us there'd be no more water delivered till next day, when the tank would be driven away and returned filled.

A little while later the crackling noise came through the loudspeakers, which meant that Captain Hué had another speech for us. I thought he was going to tell us that there would be an extra delivery of water that day.

'This is your district chief, Captain Hué.' As he spoke, the volume rose and fell so that we only heard some of what he was saying. But even so, I was sure he didn't mention anything about water supplies.

'Don't worry, people, this poison will not hurt you. It kills only insects, germs, bedbugs and mites. The counter-insurgents say that Government troops and allied troops want to poison you, and want to kill the green of the forest and destroy your livelihood. But this isn't true. We want to win the war for you, want to improve your welfare by killing the insects which bring infection, disease, and death to your children. Please allow your friends to work here without harassment.'

'But we don't have bedbugs!' said my grandmother. 'We've *never* had bedbugs!'

But, quite soon, we did get bedbugs, in spite of the white powder. My mother said we probably caught them from some of the new arrivals, who didn't look very clean. Even we weren't as clean as we used to be. When we lived in the village, we always went down to the river and washed three times a day. But now, this wasn't possible. Even though there were more people, there was always the same amount of water.

Our bean seedlings began to turn yellow and ragged-looking. Unless they could be properly planted out soon in the earth, they would shrivel up. So when a man appeared in our row selling fresh vegetables, my mother bartered our seedlings in exchange for some tomatoes and a bundle of greens.

As the camp increased, it was harder to find one's way about. The tracks between the tents all looked the same. The tents all looked the same. Small children wandered too far from their own tent and got lost.

I passed a mother, frantic for her lost child, in one row, and in the next row along, a lost little toddler was whimpering. So I led it by the hand carefully back the way it seemed to want to go, to the mother who was shrieking. But when I handed over the little boy, the mother turned on me angrily.

'That's not mine, you fool! That's somebody else's.'

Luckily Mai was still too young to crawl, so she was never lost.

There was one child, a boy of about my own age, who'd been put on the wrong truck with his baby brother, and so lost contact with his entire family, even his cousins and distant aunts. He wandered forlornly about camp carrying the little boy on his back, begging for food and asking people if they knew which camp the other trucks had been sent to.

My mother shooed him away from our tent.

'We can't give him rice,' she said. 'We've hardly enough as it is.

Anyway, he's not from our village. We can't do anything. The authorities must sort it out.'

I felt glad that I hadn't been left destitute, with nobody in the world except for a baby brother clinging round my neck.

Near the entrance gate, a command centre was set up. It was a large yellow tent, where the officers gathered around a folding wooden table, and tried to look important while they drank cold beer. The bottles of beer were kept in a metal cooling-box full of chips of ice.

My mother went to the command tent.

'At home, I would go to our headman with this problem. But we have no headman here, or friends, so I must come to you.'

There was only one American sitting outside the command centre drinking, and he didn't understand her.

'My family and I,' she went on, 'wish to be returned to our own village. We've been here quite long enough.' She had the goat with her, on a string, because she hoped it might find a blade or two of grass to eat, or perhaps somebody's vegetables when they weren't looking.

'Listen, lady, I'm sorry, but I can't do nothing for you.' The American waved his hand vaguely towards the middle of the camp. 'Go to one of your own people. Your little captain, he'll be out there some place. You go speaky him.'

My mother repeated her request. 'And another thing,' she went on. 'There's not enough food for us, or our livestock. Look at my goat! She's so hungry her milk's drying up!' The goat had begun to chew at the legs of the wooden chair the soldier was sitting on. 'People are even having to sleep with their pigs! It's disgusting!' She worked herself up, thinking of more and more to complain about. But since the man couldn't understand, there wasn't much point.

So she sat down beside him on one of the officers' folding wooden chairs, tying the goat's string to the back of the chair.

The soldier called out to another man walking past.

'Hey you! Go and find that little lieutenant. We got a mighty angry peasant woman here, and by the looks of her, she ain't moving till she gets what she wants, though I'm damned if I know what that is.'

One hour later Captain Nguyen arrived. He listened politely to my mother.

'Madam, very soon there'll be much better conditions. I'm sorry and if I could change things for you this moment, I certainly would. But as you'll soon hear over the public education system, we're doing all we can to assist you. Where's your husband? Perhaps he should do a little more of the heavy work? He could be asked to fetch your water and carry it back to the tent?'

'My husband isn't here.'

'But he should be with you. If he's with the VC, you should try to call him in. If he comes back of his own accord, he won't be harmed. We've extended the Open Arms programme for another week. All returnees who willingly give themselves up will be rewarded with an extra bag of rice as a gesture of friendship from the allies. You have a family. Wouldn't you like extra rice to feed them?'

'Even if I knew where my husband was, how could I get in touch with him while I'm imprisoned here?'

'You aren't imprisoned. You're a refugee. You're merely temporarily interned at night for your own safety. But you're perfectly free to come and go during the day.'

'Internee. Refugee. Just words. It all means the same thing. It doesn't make any difference what you call it. We're still prisoners.'

She untied the goat, hitched Mai up onto her hip and walked back to our tent. Her back was straight, her head up, her steps dignified and her spirit was not yet totally crushed.

Whatever Captain Nguyen may have said, my mother was right. We were nothings. Units. Numbers on ID cards, the inhabitants of Tent 6, Row A. We were imprisoned not just within the fence, but in time. Nothing happened. Nothing changed. Nothing grew. We had no present, and no future, and even the past was beginning to disappear. It was the same for everybody. Around us, we saw people already sinking into emptiness, and hopelessness. The family two tents along no longer bothered to dip their rice bowls and sticks into boiling water before eating. They didn't wash their hands any more. Even when pieces of food fell into the dust, they picked them up and ate them. They sat and stared at nothing all day.

'We've got to do something,' said my mother, 'before we become like that.'

'What sort of thing?'

'I don't know yet. But I'm going to think of something. Perhaps we should try and leave. Probably we'll have to try and get home.'

5

Aunt Claire's husband drove me home, and they didn't say anything about the night before, didn't ask questions, didn't press me. They were trying to be good, understanding parents. I could feel them thinking that I was under stress. They'd put too much on to me, so now they were going to have to treat me carefully.

But when I did ask questions, now they answered them.

'He was a refugee, wasn't he?' I said.

'Hm,' said Tony. 'Well, yes, I suppose so, technically he still is. He has no political status, either in this country or anywhere. Until he's legally adopted. Then he becomes British.'

I looked at Ha, glued myopically to the TV screen, his mouth half open, dribbling a little with excitement at the activities of a yoga expert, and I wondered if having political status would make any difference to him.

'If this house fell down, would *we* become refugees?'

'No, of *course* not darling!' said Patti. 'Anyway, it won't fall down.'

'If we *were* turned out of it, say, by the Army?'

'I can't see what the Army would want with it,' said Tony. 'It's hardly Sandhurst.'

'But what if they did? And we had nowhere to go? Would that make us refugees?'

'It's all a very hypothetical question. But yes, we'd be — not refugees — but evacuees. Wouldn't we, Tony? Families were evacuated like that during the war.'

'Which war?' They always talk of that war as though it were the only war. 'Tony, if there was a war here, another war, how would we know which was the right side to be on? How can you tell — if you're caught in the middle — which *is* the right side?'

'You have to ask your conscience.'

'What if your conscience can't tell you? What if both sides seem equally wrong? What if you know you're going to lose either way?'

'All very hypothetical questions, Simon. I think you'd find that in a real situation, rather than mere speculation, your conscience speaks clearly enough. Besides, if such a thing did happen, your mother and I would be here to advise you.'

We ate quietly. Ha was learning to manage the spoon, more or less, and only spilled about half the food down his front. He never chewed, but stuffed his mouth until it was stretched full, then gave one enormous swallow. It was a wonder he didn't choke. And the parents restrained themselves not to give him all the attention, not to endlessly try to correct him, but to carry on as though it was perfectly normal to have a great boy sitting at table, pouring food down himself, and occasionally going blue in the face from putting too much in and lumps getting stuck in his throat.

'He had a mother,' I said. 'She wasn't really on either side.'

'Of course he did,' said Patti soothingly. 'Or he wouldn't be here. Everybody has to have a mother at the beginning.'

'I mean a *real* mother who looked after him, and loved him. What happened to her? Wherever they found him, they must have found his mother too. Did she die, or what?'

'No, Simon, there was no mother. He was in an orphanage. They were all orphaned there.'

'Ha wasn't.'

'Sometimes mothers didn't actually die, but were forced to abandon their babies if they couldn't cope.'

'*His* mother wouldn't have. She loved him. She kept him. She used to give him her share of rice, and hardly eat any herself.'

'I'm afraid a lot of the city bar-girls had unwanted illegitimate babies, and left them in orphanages. It's what always happens when there are a lot of soldiers about.'

'Ha's mother *wasn't* a bar-girl! She wasn't! She was a farmer.'

I knew it with complete certainty. But I didn't know why I knew. And he hadn't been alone. There had been another child with him, I was sure.

'Simon, darling, it doesn't matter. You mustn't mind, even if his mother *was* that sort of person. It doesn't reflect on him in any way. He is who he is. We love him for himself, not because of what his mother did, or didn't do.'

'But it does matter that you get it *right*.' To say she was a

99

bar-girl when she was a farmer was getting it deliberately wrong.

'You went there, Patti, didn't you, to the place where Ha was found? Claire told me. Are you *sure* his mother didn't come with him?'

'Quite sure. I worked there for nearly two months. Nobody came to see him.'

'Something must have happened to her. She wouldn't have abandoned him.'

'Yes, dear. More toast?' She was humouring me. They didn't believe in Ha's mother.

6

Coils of barbed wire were laid along the flat earth between the two lines of fencing already in place. The perimeter was being strengthened again. This, so the loudspeaker crackled at us, was to protect us from the dangers of night-time murderers. The men handling the coils of barbed wire wore thick leather gauntlets.

During the day, as Captain Nguyen Hué had reminded my mother, we were free to come and go through the gates, which had to be kept open for the water carriers and the Americans' jeeps. But the camp had been created in the middle of nowhere, miles from the nearest hamlet, so unless you had a pig and wanted to walk it through the dry scrub to forage for roots, there was nowhere to go out to. Beyond the fence was all military territory. The Government soldiers had brown tents like ours to live in. The Americans had wooden huts. And all day, jeeps and trucks, carts and lorries drove up and down the dirt road delivering supplies to the American camp. Inside their wooden huts, so people said, the Americans had running water, showers, electric lamps, beds, and free supplies of food, beer, and cigarettes.

Women and children who'd been traders before began to set up stalls to sell drinks to soldiers who went past. The Americans liked canned beer and coloured fruit-drinks. Most of the drink on sale had to be stolen from PX army supplies. There wasn't any other way you could get it. I wondered why the Americans would want to buy back from our people their own drinks, at double the price.

My mother said it was because they had nothing better to do with their money.

She said that every American was paid thousands of piastres each month, on top of having all his meals free, just for being a soldier. If they were paid so much, it explained why they wanted to come here in the first place. I could not think of any other reason why anybody would want to go and live in somebody else's land.

Some of the wooden huts had painted signs up on them. *Hollywood Bar*, they said, or *Snack Bar Sexy*, or *Sunset Boulevard*.

During the afternoons, girls who were young and pretty could go there and earn money. The Americans called them the boom-boom girls.

The woman in the next tent to us dressed her eldest daughter in a new yellow silk *ao dai,* put colour on her lips and cheeks, and led her to the hut marked *Sundown Tropicana* where the girl made six hundred piastres in one afternoon. But the next day she made only two hundred. You only earned the top price the first time.

The Americans thought that every girl in the whole camp was ready for boom-boom. Even while I was standing by the fence watching the traffic going past and swirling up the dust, a truck pulled up and the driver shouted in my own language.

'You boy! Sister?'

He threw a candy bar over the fence to me. We'd nearly come to the end of our rice, and I was hungry, so I picked it up and unwrapped it.

'You got number one very good sister?'

I nodded.

'What her name?'

'Mai,' I said.

'See these kids,' he said to the man in the cab with him. 'They'll do anything for money, if you treat them right. Even sell their sisters.' He took out a handful of notes and waved them at me.

'Hey, you boy. Come. I give you candy bar. Three o'clock, you bring me pretty number one boom-boom. I give you ten piastres.'

I didn't tell my mother but I told the woman in the tent next to us and she took her daughter to the meeting place. But I didn't even get another candy bar from the soldier, let alone the money he promised. At night there was curfew.

As the sun began to go down, red through a haze of dust, softening the drab brown tents and the wooden huts of *Tropicana* and *Snack Bar Sexy* to a rosy glow, there'd be a scurrying of pig owners, traders, and boom-boom girls towards the gates. Everybody has to be back inside the enclosure before dusk when the gates were closed and two Government soldiers stood guard. The Americans went back to their wooden huts where they had film shows and music every night.

In our tents in the evenings, we had stories. My grandmother had always been a story-teller. She knew stories about princesses, dragons, magic mountains, mandarins, enchanted pagodas, and poor woodcutters. She knew the story of the Betel Nut and the Areca Tree, the Tale of the Golden Tortoise, and the story of the Buffalo Boy and the Banyan Tree. I often thought I'd heard every story she had in her head, and then she'd surprise me with a new one.

She always began quietly, almost as though talking to herself. As soon as I heard the first muttering of: 'Once there lived a wise mandarin who had two sons,' or 'Once, long ago, in the time of the dynasty of Le, in the village of Bich Cau,' I would go and sit down close to her and listen carefully. When the children in the next tent heard her begin a story, they too would creep into our tent and settle down by grandmother's stool.

She never took any notice of an audience. Even if somebody interrupted with a question, or if Mai started crying, she went on as though she were alone.

One evening she was telling us a story about a fairy queen who gave a great banquet in the Land of Bliss to a visiting mortal. The table was abundantly laid with numerous dishes of the very best food. My grandmother described each of them, in detail — the pure white rice-cakes sweetened with honey, the duck-liver patés studded with diamonds of pork, the roast peacock decorated with its own aquamarine feathers, the rich mango sauces, the golden fruit heaped on lacquered bowls. For days, we had nothing but plain rice with sometimes some vegetables, so it was good to hear about delicious food even if we could not really eat it. But my mother didn't seem to think so. She came into the tent in the middle of the story. She only listened for a moment before she put her hands over her ears and began to shout at my grandmother to shut up.

'Why must you tell stories like that? You cruel old woman! You only do it to make me feel bad. But it's not *my* fault I can't give you proper meals. You know I can't help it. So don't reproach me like that, by teasing the children. Don't ever tell that story again, not while we're here.'

I wanted to tell my mother that, even when we were hungry, we liked hearing about the magic feast, but she seemed so upset that I didn't dare say anything. My mother never used to get angry with my grandmother. She always treated her with kindness and gentleness. I think she was ashamed afterwards, because she brewed my grandmother some tea, even though we had hardly any fuel left. While they sat crouched over the tiny glow of the fire, I curled up on my mat at the back of the tent and pretended to be asleep, but behind my closed eyes, I went back to the peace and security of home.

First, I walked slowly back from helping in the fields. I passed a buffalo wallowing in muddy water, its whole body submerged, except for its broad back and curved horns. Then through the village, stepping over a dog which lazed, panting, in the shade of a mango tree. Past the bicycle repair shop and the schoolhouse, and the trim little houses, till I reached our own. In the glade behind, I saw the bright white of the ancestors' tombs through the green of the leaves.

I walked into our grassy yard and peered into the coop to see if there were any eggs. The hen clucked angrily and I could smell the sour fragrance of droppings mingled with dried grass. I drew out one cream-coloured egg, still warm.

I saw my mother cooking at the side of the house. She was reaching up to take a bamboo sieve from a hook overhead. Her long, black hair was caught up in a coil at the back of her head. Her loose white shirt caught the light, like the newly whitened tombstones beyond. Her trousers were loosely rolled half-way up her legs. She was very beautiful and very serious. But then, she glanced up and smiled. She didn't smile often, but when she did it was like a welcome.

My father must have been there. I couldn't see him. But I heard his voice, speaking to my mother in murmurings of gentle chatter, so I stayed outside so as not to disturb them.

The sun was slanting in through the open side, casting a square of light on the smooth earth floor. On the window-shelf stood a row of sprouting bean seedlings, each in its little ball of damp earth. Through the window I saw my grandmother sorting dried beans into a tin bowl, the bad ones to throw out for the hens, and the good ones to be soaked and prepared for cooking.

Every detail was clear, the shape of each leaf, the contour of each tree, the deep shade cast by the overhanging thatch of each house, even the flower pattern on the side of grandmother's tin bowl. The village and the fields, and the tombs of the ancestors, were all neat and well cared for.

Then I fell asleep and dreamed about going home, but now it was different. As I walked towards the village, everything faded before me. There were no houses, only rubble and broken walls, and scattered over all the rubble were paper leaflets.

I bent to pick one up.

Greetings, Friends! Your families who were formerly living in this village have taken refuge with the allies.

As I read it, I did not know which language it was printed in, theirs or ours, because in my dream both had become mixed up.

> They have been supplied with money, rice and good places to live. Their health is being taken care of by doctors who give them all kinds of medicines every day. Come back, friends, and live peacefully with your wives, sisters, mothers and children. The Government is ready to welcome you. Together, we can build a strong, rich nation.

I looked up to see who else might come to read these hundreds of leaflets. But I was quite alone in an empty world and everything began to disintegrate like it sometimes does in dreams, so that I was almost glad to wake to the reality of another morning in camp.

A group of Americans came round asking us questions. They weren't soldiers and, unlike soldiers, they spoke our language. My mother said they were spies but the woman in the next tent said they were charity workers who wanted to bring us gifts of American wheat and machines and medicines, and didn't want to fight with us.

They wandered down the rows, smiling and nodding at people and touching small children on the head. They stopped at our tent and squatted down by my grandmother who was holding Mai, and asked:

'And what do you think of the situation here?'

My grandmother was so surprised at hearing one of the big round-eyes speaking her own language that for a few moments she was shaken out of her lethargy.

'We were forced to come here,' she mumbled. 'The men came to our village so often. Twice or three times it was the men from the North. You foreigners came many times too. Each time we suffered. Your people came last and brought us here. You ask me what *I* think of it? I wanted to be left alone, as I was. What's to become of the tombs? Who'll take care of them now?'

She closed her eyes to show that the conversation was over. The group round her tried to look sympathetic. Then they turned to my mother who was fanning a small glow of charcoal embers under our black cooking pot. It was cheap rice handed out by the soldiers. Since we had nearly nothing else left we had to eat it.

'What are you cooking, madam?' one of them asked her politely, but it was a silly question since it was obvious what was in the pot.

'Rice,' said my mother, without looking at them. 'Pig rice!'

The leader of the group began to explain why they had come to our camp. They were concerned about the living conditions here, and wanted to know about the people's feelings at having to be moved from their villages. What did my mother think the people here needed most of all? What did they want? What skills did she have which could be used to make things to sell so she could make money to feed her family better? My mother answered only one of the questions, the last.

'I'm not a trader. I'm a farmer. I don't wish to make things to sell. I have only one thing to sell. I have a daughter.' She pointed to Mai sleeping in grandmother's lap. 'I could wait here till she's old enough, and then sell her to your people in the *Hawaii Bar*.'

The group shuffled uneasily and changed the subject:

'When do you think the war will end?'

'How can I answer that sort of question!' my mother snapped. 'It isn't our war. It's yours. I have two children to care for and grandmother. I don't know whether my husband is alive or dead. These worries take all my time. Go and ask the old men. They have time to sit about all day and think up answers to riddles.'

The sloping canvas of the tent roof flapped with a twanging noise, and the poles creaked as they strained against the wind. Outside, pieces of tattered rubbish raced down the paths, before they spiralled high into the air like coloured kites. The wind was hot and every day it grew stronger.

We would have to strengthen our home and make it watertight before the rain started. As the wind blew, we could smell the smell of the American's grilled meat wafting over from their camp, and we saw them lining up to collect their midday meal on paper plates.

'Cheap Charlie!' two children screamed at them through the fence. 'You number ten cheap Charlie!'

I walked round camp with my eyes to the ground looking for something that could be used to make protective walls against the coming storms. Others were already doing the same, gathering any scraps they could find — bits of corrugated iron, packing cases, sheets of plastic, flattened beer cans. Even bundles of straw, or strips of old rag could be woven into a screen.

I watched a scuffle when two children saw the same empty cigarette pack in the dust. But while they fought for it, another boy calmly claimed it for himself and disappeared into the canvas maze.

Every piece of rubbish seemed to have been already seized. So I went round to the fence. Plenty of useful things usually blew across from the Americans' huts and became caught against the outer wire, and there I saw something better than a mere piece of cardboard or plastic. It was a large, wooden plank which had slid off the back of a passing truck. Another boy saw it too. We stared at each other with determination. He moved off first, darting through the camp, towards the gates, to get round the outer fence

107

and try to reach the plank before me. He moved so fast I knew I'd never overtake him. However, the direct route to the plank, through the double fences and the barbed wire, was hardly any distance at all.

Wriggling under the first fence was easy because pigs had been rootling there and softened the earth. Running across the open patch was easy too. I was already half-way to the plank and my rival wasn't even in sight. But I still had to get through the barbed wire. The coils were as tall as a man, arching above my head, higher than they'd seemed and broader and springier as though each strand had a life of its own. As I parted two strands to slip myself between, the loops of wire snapped shut, tearing my forearm like thorns, and biting into my bare feet like scorpions. The more I struggled to free myself, the more tightly I became entangled.

I watched, helplessly imprisoned, as the other boy, panting, reached the plank, picked it up, then looked round to see where I'd got to. He saw me ensnared in the coils. He grinned and waved, before striding off with the plank on his shoulder, but he must have told somebody I was there, because much later two soldiers came with an enormous pair of wire-cutters to set me free. They thought it was funny, and laughed, but they wore strong boots and heavy canvas jackets protecting their flesh.

My mother asked me how I had got so cut about and I had to explain about the plank of wood that we might have used.

'There's no point in bothering with all that,' she said. 'We won't be here when the rains come. We'll be setting off before long.'

I was so excited that I tried to dream about home again. But this time, I couldn't see anything at all, not even rubble. Where our homes had once been was only flattened earth.

Anyway, by the next day, my mother had changed her mind. 'We can't go. Grandma's sick. She's too ill to travel.'

She was ill because of the rice rations we were being given.

They gave us a small ration each day, but it wasn't fresh. It was always soft rice.

My mother explained to me that because my grandmother was old, she wasn't as strong as us, and her stomach wouldn't accept the bad rice. To help her regain her strength she needed fresh, simple food which she could easily digest.

The woman in the next tent said the rice was so bad that it wasn't even fit to feed to her pig, let alone her youngest baby who had reached the age to be weaned. So after my grandmother had been ill with stomach cramps for three days my mother and the woman next to us both went along to the yellow command centre tent to ask if the rice could be improved. One of the American officers was there. He wouldn't believe that the rice was bad.

'But *he* doesn't have to eat it!' my mother said. 'He has his own kind of food.'

The interpreter explained what my mother had said.

'*Sure* I'll eat it,' said the man. He had a huge, round stomach, and great fat fingers like bananas. He told one of his men to go and fetch a bowl of the rice we were complaining about, and he'd prove how good it was, and when the rice was brought, he began to eat it with a fork, smiling all the time.

'See, it's great!' He made loud noises of pleasure as he finished the bowlful down to the last grain. 'Gee, that was so good, Captain, I think I can guess why your people like eating rice every day. Now you tell them I really enjoyed that.'

Captain Nguyen, who had to eat from the same rice supply as us, knew as well as we did that the rice was bad, and he didn't translate what the fat American said.

Soon it wasn't only my grandmother who was ill. Mai, too, lay still, her eyes dull, staring at nothing. She didn't wave her hands about and babble. Her eyes didn't follow me. She didn't smile. When my mother tried to encourage her to feed, she didn't even bother to turn her cheek away from the nipple.

My mother boiled up some herbs for her and spooned the liquid mixture into Mai's mouth, but she could hardly swallow. We took her to the command centre tent.

'My baby's very ill, and I must have help.' Luckily, there was a Government soldier there who spoke our language.

'The allied doctor'll be here in the afternoon. He'll see all internees and dependants. Come back then.'

'I don't think she'll survive till then. Please find someone quickly.'

At home we sometimes had small fevers but they always passed within a few days. We didn't have bad fevers which made children die.

The soldier finally went off and fetched an American who wore a white band with a red cross on his shirt sleeve and carried the medical box, and an interpreter.

The man with the medical box examined Mai, looked in her mouth and into her eyes, felt her wrist.

'I guess the kid's only got a touch of malaria,' he said. 'Tell her it's nothing serious, give it lots of fluid, keep it cool.'

'But she won't take anything I give her, and marsh fever is very dangerous for a small baby,' said my mother. 'If it's marsh fever she needs medicine.'

People who travelled through the forest sometimes got ill with malaria because of mosquitoes in stagnant pools. But in our village we never had it. The mosquitoes couldn't live in the river water because it flowed too fast, nor in the paddy water because it was too muddy.

'Sure she needs medicine!' said the medical assistant. 'She needs quinine. But I don't have none.' He opened up the medical box and pointed rather helplessly into it. 'All we have here is iodine and Band-aids, and some lozenges for mouth ulcers. We don't carry quinine in the boxes. And even if we did I'm not even trained. Somebody explain to her, I'm only a paramedic.'

'But this is my baby girl,' said my mother. 'She's sick because we're here. We didn't ask to come here for our babies to get sick. Please, please help me. Are you going to wait till all our children die first before you do anything? Every day you keep telling us you're saving us from being killed; what's the point in saving us if our babies are going to die anyway?' Then she began to cry.

'OK, OK, calm down.' The soldier with the red cross on his arm patted her on the shoulder. 'I'll see if I can find some quinine for the kid. You sit tight here and I'll be right on back.'

The interpreter drank a bottle of beer out of the icebox in the command centre tent while we waited. The medical soldier came back quite quickly, not leisurely like some of the soldiers but running. He must have seen how ill Mai was. He prepared a syringe which he plunged into Mai's thigh. I saw the long, thin needle slide in, but Mai didn't even cry. He told the interpreter to explain what he was doing.

'Tell her that's an anti-malarial shot I just gave her baby,' he said. 'She'll be OK now, but to carry on making her take fluids. That's very important. Or she'll be dehydrated. Get her back on the breast as soon as possible.'

Other people had realized that medical treatment was already being offered and had begun to crowd round, asking for help. There were several children who had skin sores and there was a girl with a broken wrist. Soon there was quite a crowd, and since they wouldn't go away, the command centre officers decided to fetch the doctor and begin the afternoon treatment session straight away.

Mai brightened quite quickly and took a small feed, then she went to sleep while my mother lay resting on her mat with Mai in her arms.

But when Mai woke up she seemed much worse. She trembled violently as though wild spirits had taken hold of her. Her eyes rolled back, her legs kept jerking, and she was making horrible noises. My mother ran with Mai through the camp back to where the doctor and the medical assistant were still giving out treatment. Anybody with an ID card was being attended to.

But by the time we got there, Mai had stopped jerking and was quite limp, with her head thrown back and her eyes closed. My mother pushed to the front of the queue and held Mai out to the man who had injected her with the medicine. He examined her quickly.

'Lordy, I think she's died,' he said, and handed her over to the doctor.

'What did you give her?' the doctor said.

'Only one milligram. Quinine.'

'I guess she maybe was allergic to the shot.'

'How was I to know she'd have an allergy?'

'She might have died anyhow. You did quite right.'

'But what in heck do I do now?'

'Give her compensation. She can have some more. Some of these people, they care more about losing a pig than a child.'

8

Cheerful music began to play out through the loudspeakers. Then Captain Nguyen Hué's voice was back.

'This is Captain Nguyen Hué, your area chief. I have good news. Many of you are to be relocated further south to a good place situated nearer food supplies and medical attention, and safer from the enemy. There you will be able to live in peace. And the government will be giving each family compensation of five thousand piastres, so you can begin to farm again, just as before. Transportation will begin in a few days. So please do not wander but remain near your families at all times. Remember, the Government never forgets its people.'

The music blared on.

'We must start for home in the morning,' said my mother quietly.

We couldn't travel without money, but if we sold our goat or any of our household possessions to other camp-dwellers, it might arouse their suspicions. There were so many spies about, you never knew who to trust. Although she had no silk *ao dai*, my mother put on a clean shirt and coloured her lips, and in the afternoon she went to the wooden hut called *Snack Bar Sexy* and earned two hundred piastres for our journey.

In the morning, as soon as the gates were unlocked, I went outside the fence. At first, I stood about watching the traffic, then I wandered into the nearby scrub pretending to gather twigs and dry leaves. I ambled further and further away from the fence and when I felt sure that no one was watching, I dropped down into a slight dip in the ground, where I was half-hidden behind a scraggy bush, and I waited there till my mother came out at midday, also pretending to collect kindling. But in her basket, underneath the sticks, she had a ball of cooked rice to last us for that day, as well as a small bag of loose rice. She dropped down beside me.

'But what about Grandma?'

'She's much better today. She's sleeping at the moment. I left her some rice for tonight.'

I'd thought she'd be coming with us. Now I knew she wasn't, I wished that I'd said goodbye.

We waited all day, lying quite still in the dry, oppressive heat, and hoping that nobody would notice us.

Towards evening, the bleakness of camp and the drab colours of the tents began to soften and change to a pink glow in the dusty sunset. We watched people hurrying back towards the gates to be inside the enclosure before curfew.

As it grew dark, the camp became lit by dots of flickering light, as each family made their tiny fire to cook rice. Each fire was a warm bright star.

While they were preparing to eat, to tell stories, to lie down and rest, we were going to run away into the night. I felt frightened and lonely and I wanted to be back inside the safety of the fence. My mother must have sensed my reluctance to leave, for she held my hand firmly as she helped me to my feet. Our people are supposed never to leave the tombs of our ancestors. Now we were leaving behind my grandmother even before she was dead.

'And what good would it do her if we stayed? But if we go home and make ourselves safe, then we can come back later and rescue her.'

9

We walked all night. There were fireflies dancing and darting, iridescent green underneath the trees. When I was tired, she carried me on her back. When even she was too tired to walk a step further, we stopped and I lay down to sleep.

'Just for an hour,' she said. 'No more. I'll wake you when it's time.'

I rested my head on the bag of rice and went to sleep safe in my mother's love. She cared for me more than for any of the others. She had chosen to take me with her. Until we found my father, she loved me best of all. I could sleep safely.

'Ha! Don't go to sleep. I want to know what happened. Stop pretending you don't understand.'

'But I don't know what happened. Ask someone else.'

My mother shook me to wake me. I wanted her to leave me alone and let me go on sleeping. I was so comfortable lying in a nest of dry leaves, under the trees. The fireflies had gone and it was nearly light.

'You've had enough sleep. You must wake up. We've got to move on now.'

The sleep had been too short.

We followed a road running through the middle of a rubber plantation. The trees were tall and graceful with silvery bark. They didn't grow like the tangled trees of the forest but were in straight, orderly lines, one after another, ahead, behind, and on both sides, the lines so straight it was as though they had been drawn on paper with a pen.

At first a cold grey mist hovered between the trunks. Then, as the day grew hotter, the mist dissolved and the heavy canopy of leaves overhead shaded us from the sun.

When we reached the smoke-house and the planters' houses at the centre of the plantation we heard a lot of activity of men and machines. The air was filled with the grating and high-pitched whining of engines. My mother wasn't sure if it was safe to go on and we hesitated on the road. But a soldier driving a yellow bulldozer shouted down to her, above the roaring of the engine:

114

'Hurry on! This is a clearance zone! Keep moving!'

So we hurried on and nobody stopped us. So long as we kept walking along the track, we were no concern of theirs.

The soldiers were at work with huge mechanical equipment uprooting the rubber plantation, starting at the centre and working outwards. They had power saws, and earth-movers on tracks, and bulldozers which pushed and pulled at the silvery trunks. The trees were strong, but the machines were stronger, and nudged and grappled tirelessly until the roots weakened, rocked, and finally gave way. And as each tree fell, the cool, leafy shade became an open space of broken wood and twisted roots.

'But what are they doing it *for*?' I said.

'Ssh,' said my mother, holding my hand. 'Don't take any notice. Don't look at them. Just keep walking.'

The smaller saplings and the shrubs were cut down by soldiers striding down the rows slashing at each branch, one thrust with a sharp blade, then another, and it was down. The ground was a mass of billowing leaves and jagged branches. And thick smoke rose in black columns as trees and leaves were burned. Anything still left standing was being bulldozed.

Then, above the noise of machinery we heard the thundering of an approaching air-raid. My mother pushed me into the ditch beside the road and flung herself on top of me. But after a few minutes when we looked out, we saw that the demolition workers in the plantation were ignoring the explosions and were calmly proceeding with their work as though their lives were in no danger. So we climbed up and went on walking, and further on we saw the cause of the noise. Some of the plantation buildings were being blown up, not by aircraft overhead but by a group of soldiers standing at some distance from each building.

They were fine, strong buildings built of brick, with verandas and steps, shuttered windows, metal roofing and gutters, and little flower gardens laid out in front of each.

The order to detonate was given by a leader. A silent wait for half a moment, and then the walls would appear to shiver and in a shower of dust and bricks, the whole building would spurt upwards and be gone. One by one the buildings were being reduced to rubble.

Beyond the brick buildings was a cluster of smaller wood and thatch huts. I saw the soldiers pour kerosene from a can over the roofs and set them alight with flaming torches. Another group of people, surrounded by their possessions, stood watching their homes going up in flames. They made no resistance. They didn't speak, nor try to stop the soldiers burning their homes, just stood and stared as though mesmerized by the brilliant red flames and the dense smoke.

The smoke changed direction, and the soldiers moved the group and their belongings further away and sat them in two rows in a clearing. Then another soldier, with several cameras round his neck on straps, ran through the smoke to the burning huts and took photographs of them. Long ago, I had seen a soldier photograph an old man who had been shot off his bicycle. First destroy, then photograph.

We were glad to leave the plantation behind. We walked for the rest of that day, encouraging each other when we were tired. But we never reached our own village. It was too far and there was too much traffic on the road. At dusk, we stopped at a hamlet to rest.

Rach Bap was a messy and uncared-for looking place, and half the homes seemed to be deserted. We shouldn't have stayed there. But we didn't choose it. My mother was so tired that she hadn't even the strength to carry our bundle.

We should have known that it wasn't safe to stay anywhere. We should have travelled on and risked snakes and scorpions under logs and slept in the forest. Or we should have struggled on until we found my father. Instead, we stopped at Rach Bap, where life seemed quieter than in any other place we'd passed. We went to the headman who led us to a house where we could stay. My mother negotiated the deal and paid with two American wrist-watches she had in the bag of rice. The people took us in as though resigned to strangers, but they hardly spoke to us at all.

I was put to sleep on the floor of the main room where the baby of the family was in a cloth hammock over my head, and was rocked to sleep by an old woman.

When the hammock began to sway backwards and forwards, I should have known that we shouldn't stay. I should have warned my mother. But even when I knew things with such clarity and such certainty, I was never able to explain them to anybody else. It was my own knowledge, wrapped up inside me.

All night there were the scrabblings of rats in the thatch overhead, the buzz of mosquitoes, the cries of night creatures in the forest, and the quiet breathing of the other people. Overhead, every time the baby stirred in his sleep, he set his hammock into a gentle rhythm of movement. Rock, rock, swing, swing.

116

Without any sounds of warning that they were coming, the men were standing silhouetted in the doorway. Just like a day when a black-skinned man shot a good laying hen. It was so familiar that it seemed hardly worth bothering about. It would be better to go back to sleep.

'Why were we there, sir?'

'We were there on infantry mission. To move forward into enemy-controlled territory, to 711833. There, to find, to close with, and to neutralize.'

'Not that. I mean, why were we there at all? What were we doing in that country? Why did they bundle us into planes, fly us half-way round the world, and put us down in the middle of some weird place?'

'Go write to your Congressman about it. I didn't draft you in.'

'And why were we moving out?'

'On account of I said so. Is that good enough answer, troop? Tomorrow we go to Rach Bap. I believe in America and all that is honest and true. Now go read *The Limits of Intervention*. That'll give you an answer or two. I got a wife and two kids back home. And right now, I'm on short-timer's stick and I'm going to see them again and I don't care how I get to it.'

'You mean you'd zap 'em? Waste 'em?'

'What d'you think I mean? You think killing in war's something new?'

'We can't do that.'

'Aw come on, buddy. This is a Free Strike Zone. You can do anything in Free Strike Zone. That's what it's all about. Arvin invited us in here, OK? So when in Free Strike, we strike free. OK? We're not fanatics. We're just good boys doing the job we were trained for. And these people in this hamlet have cheated out on us.'

They were wondering what to do about us. You could see they were because they were arguing among themselves. Then the leader gave an order.

'Take care of these people,' he said. 'And I mean care,' and he walked away.

They lined us up near a ditch. I didn't realize what they were going to do until too late. And when I did realize, my feet seemed fixed to the ground and wouldn't move.

They wasted us. It was a small incident to them in the middle of a much bigger one. We mishandled the situation. We did not resist when we should have. So it was our fault. As a group, of women, children, old men and babies, we were too docile, or too proud. We handled it all wrong. Perhaps when they lined us up, we should have shouted a bit, answered them back, screamed, sworn at them. Then they might have seen that we, too, were people. But we didn't. They said, 'Line up over there,' and we went. We were stony-faced and impassive, so they couldn't see us as humans, only as some kind of lower creature from the forest.

Then it was absolutely silent and dark. My body was wet all over, sticky, drenched. There was a terrible pain in my arm, and I couldn't move it, and a heavy weight on top of me. But I knew exactly where I was and, with my good arm, I felt for the switch and when the light was on, I saw that the stickiness wasn't blood. There was no red. The wet was pee, soaking warm and wet, and the weight on me was Ha. The pain in my arm wasn't a wound, but Ha's heavy skull lying across it, giving me cramp.

He wasn't moving. He was cold. I was sure he was dead in my bed. I shook him and his black eyelashes quivered, and he muttered something incomprehensible in his sleep, but he didn't wake, only snuggled closer to me.

'What are you doing in my bed? How d'you get up here?' I shifted my arm from under him. 'Look, you've peed in my bed, you horrible thing. Why not go and wet your own stinky bed?'

He opened his eyes and smiled at me. 'Shimoo. Nice bed. Nice boy. Like you.'

I edged away from him. His breath smelled too. I slithered down from the bed, removed my wet pyjamas and slept the rest of the night on the floor. No wet, no rocking, just cold and hard.

At breakfast, I watched Ha stack six Weetabix up on his bowl like a brick tower, then attack them with his spoon, like a karate expert, so that flakes and drops of milk exploded across the table. Now that they openly admit he's the same age as me, they don't keep tying bibs round his neck.

'I thought he'd died in the night,' I said.

'I expect it was a dream, darling,' said Patti. 'Poor you. We shouldn't have had cheese soufflé.'

History was second period. We were learning about Karl Marx, Mr Barlow's potted version. It might have been interesting but I was so tired that I ached all over, and the classroom walls swayed. I laid my head on the desk just for a moment, and fell into a deep sleep. It seemed like a whole night later that I was woken by Barlow at my desk towering over me.

'You! Boy! Is my instruction so dull that you'd rather sleep through it?'

I got a detention for insolence. Three DT's and you go to the Head. I must stay awake in class, and I must stay awake in the night. I don't want to go back to that heap in the ditch.

'Sorry about last night, darling,' said Patti.

'What?'

'Ha in your bed. I didn't realize. And all wet too.'

Why did she apologize? What for? Not your fault, mother. I wet myself. The wet in my bed was *my* wet. People do, when they're really frightened. Everything inside you collapses with terror. It's what shit-scared means.

'But it's all changed and clean now. I aired your mattress in the garden. Goodness knows how he managed to get up on to your bunk in the night.'

He was tucked up in his own bunk below, with his blue bunny wabbit in his arms.

When she came to kiss me good-night in my bunk, her cheek was exactly on a level with mine. She didn't have to bend over me. I felt ashamed to kiss her back. I wished I could tell her. It isn't just him who wets the bed. I did too when they wasted women and children.

'Good-night darling,' she said. 'Sleep tight.'

Stay here with me Patti. All night. Don't leave me. I shan't sleep. I shall keep myself awake all night. I shall risk three DT's and a trip to the Head rather than sleep.

'Yes. Good-night Patti.'

'And if he's very noisy, come and let us know.'

I didn't want to sleep, but when you're very tired, you can't help yourself.

And I found that the people who'd taken care of us didn't even hang around. They just left us, flies buzzing. It was midday. Full sun, red dust, white sky. Flies around and dogs.

A child was moving. Not even scratched. When she saw me sit up, she began to smile, and held out her arms to me.

'Ssh!' I said, as though the other people were sleeping. Besides, her cry might call the soldiers back. There were puffs of smoke like white blossom in the trees from a combat zone five klicks distant from here.

I put her back beside her mother and ran.

PART THREE
Simon and Ha

Ha always had a rotten smell about him, like decay, even when he'd just been washed. Sometimes I couldn't bear to look at him. I couldn't touch anything he'd touched. I couldn't let the skin of my hand touch the skin of his. Now that I knew where he'd been and what he'd seen, he revolted me.

'Patti,' I said. 'That baby you had, the one that died. Was it a boy or a girl?'

She was reaching for a pile of clean clothes from the airing cupboard. She looked surprised that I even knew.

'Claire told me,' I said. 'The night I spent there.' If the stillborn brother or sister had survived I wouldn't now be sharing my home, my room, my parents and my home, with Ha.

'It was a girl,' said Patti. 'A daughter. She wasn't stillborn. She lived for an hour.'

It didn't seem to me that it made much difference. 'Her birthday would've been early summer. We were going to call her May or Maisie.'

'D'you mind that Ha's not your own child? D'you sometimes wish he'd been born to you?'

'How could he be? He's quite different from us.'

'Don't you even think about it?'

'I think about his *mother* sometimes, wherever she is, and why she abandoned him. But mostly I try not to. She might suddenly change her mind and want him back.'

'I don't suppose she does,' I said.

'It was a terrible place to leave a child. No food, no medicine for the sick ones. Not enough people to help care for the children.'

'You went there, didn't you? Claire told me that too. Why didn't you tell Ha about it, what it was like there?'

'About huge rats, nearly as big as puppies, taking food off the babies' plates? And the local women coming and stealing food for their own families? Is that the sort of thing you think he should be told about?'

'If it's the *truth*.' It was beginning to seem to me that she and Tony hadn't a clue how to do the best for Ha.

'Only part of it. I only knew what I saw in one orphanage. I don't know about any of the rest. Better to let the past be the past. Anyway, Ha wouldn't possibly understand, would he?'

'It might *help* him understand better.'

'I doubt it,' said Patti vaguely. 'Come on now, time for supper.'

But Ha's pants were wet so Patti had to bath him before we could start supper. When he was dry and powdered he sat naked on the rug in our room waiting for his clean clothes. He always sat in the same place, on the edge of the rug.

I grew up with that rug. It came from my grandmother's home. I suppose Patti must have grown up with it too. It had an intricate design of stylized leaves, blossoms and flower buds, and a patterned border round the edge. And somewhere, within the tiny detail, there was a flaw, a deliberate mistake in the weaving. My grandmother told me that Muslim carpet weavers always put a fault so as not to offend Allah, because only the works of Allah are ever perfect. I used to lie and look at the rug for hours, following the pattern of the stems, the contours of the petals, the curl of each leaf, trying to work out where the weaver had made his deliberate mistake.

Patti took Ha's clean underclothes from his drawer. He had so many pairs of underpants, more than a dozen. She began to dress him.

I stepped carefully round where Ha had been squatting on my rug. His powdered bottom left a faint, dusty imprint on the wool pile. Even after the talcum powder had gone, his mark would be there for ever. I wouldn't be able to touch the rug again, even with my foot or my slipper. He had contaminated it.

I had had such a marvellous plan to help him, to read about his country, and tell him about his past. But now that I'd begun to know it, I didn't want to do anything for him.

There were places all over the house like the rug, which I couldn't touch. I couldn't get into the bath after him until I'd filled it to the brim with cold water and swished away all fragments and traces of him, and even then I didn't like to touch the sides. I couldn't hold the wooden bannister where his hands had grasped it as he came upstairs. I never touched the chair he sat on, even though Patti wiped it after meals. She could scrub away the crumbs of egg, the smears of jam, but no way could she remove the invisible stain of him.

Nor could I handle the mug Ha used. It was one of a set of six white china ones, each the same shape, but with a different coloured picture printed on the side. Ha took a fancy to the picture of a blue and red windmill. Though he'd now learned how to drink from a mug, instead of lowering his face to it, he always slurped and clinked his teeth against the china rim with a rattle like dead teeth.

Even after it had been through the heavy-soil sequence in the dishwasher, sluiced with chemical detergents, sprayed with scalding water, and triple-rinsed by rotating mechanical arms, I didn't like touching it.

Miss Spaark called while Ha was still being dressed. Tony must have let her in. She came up to our room as though it were her own home. I went on pretending to do my homework.

'Hello, Ha. Had a nice bath then?'

Ha freed himself from Patti's hold where she struggled to guide his legs into the holes of the clean underpants, and went and gave Miss Spaark a noisy kiss. He had grown very fond of kissing lately. Miss Spaark didn't seem to mind, but I thought Patti and Tony ought to teach him not to go round kissing strangers. They might get the wrong idea.

'There's my fine boy,' said Miss Spaark. 'Now let your mummy finish dressing you.' Patti went back to the battle with the underpants. 'And how are things coming along? More settled yet? He *is* a most affectionate boy, isn't he? At least you have the confidence of knowing that there's *no* malice in a child like this. He bears no grudge against the world, does he? Like some of these Down's children, basically, so gentle. Whereas some of the high IQ's we've got in care, they can be real monsters! Every trick in the book. It's the devil of a job we have placing them.'

Ha leaned against Patti as though she were a wall while Patti tried to ease his arms, suddenly stiff as sticks, down into the shirt sleeves.

Miss Spaark smirked admiringly. 'Not a wicked thought in his little head.'

I had two blue-black indentations exactly representing Ha's side teeth, where he had experimentally bitten into me when I wouldn't fetch him a piece of computer paper the instant he demanded it.

Patti gave me a quick, warning glance which seemed to ask me to demonstrate to Miss Spaark, how I didn't have a wicked thought in my head either. I wondered why. Miss Spaark didn't deserve my politeness. She didn't deserve anything. She was paid to do her job and come and coo at what she saw as nice-natured little boys. I wondered why she hadn't been told about the cat. I wondered if I should tell her.

'And how's our Simon, then?' Miss Spaark smiled at me. 'Feeling less bitter about it all? Less resentful?'

After he'd thrown Dido out of the window, I'd known I had to get rid of Ha. But now I wasn't so sure that that was the solution. So I didn't say anything about the cat.

'I never was resentful,' I said.

'It was only natural, dear, you should have felt that way. A quite understandable reaction, which I had anticipated. After all, you'd had the prime position in your parents' affections.'

'I did not resent him,' I repeated.

Being shot at with the rest of your village, and doing nothing to resist, was a worse mistake than killing a pet cat in your new home.

'You see, Simon,' Miss Spaark went on, 'at the beginning we *were* rather worried about you. It seemed you were growing bitter and twisted.'

'Simon's been absolutely *marvellous* lately,' Patti interrupted quickly. 'A real support. And so patient with Ha.'

Perhaps Miss Spaark realized she was going too far.

'That's pretty,' she said, abruptly changing the subject and admiring the rug on the floor. 'Turkish, is it?'

'It came from my mother's family,' said Patti. She was now persevering to guide Ha's resisting hands to fasten the buttons down his shirt front.

'It's got a flaw in it,' I said. 'A special mistake.'

'Really? It looks in excellent condition to me,' said Miss Spaark. 'I dare say it's worth quite something.'

'No, in the weaving. My grandmother told me. Because only Allah can be perfect.'

But Miss Spaark didn't seem interested in the techniques or religious quirks of rug-makers. She was, as usual, more interested in her own opinions of things than in mine.

At last Miss Spaark went and it was another normal sort of terrible meal to be endured. He squarked with pleasure like a parrot when food was before him, and with frustration if he couldn't consume it fast enough. And he flung food about like a pig rootling for tubers. As soon as we'd finished, he had to be taken upstairs and bathed once more, because he'd wet his pants again. I can't even remember how long it's been like this. Has he been here weeks, or months, or always.

Tony and I cleared the table and stacked the dishwasher.

'It's the exhilaration of eating,' I said. 'Makes him wet.'

'Could be. Partly that social worker's visits too. I'm beginning to think Ha understands more about the purpose of her visits than we give him credit for. He knows perfectly well why she comes.' If Ha knew that, he knew more than I did. 'And it unsettles him.'

'So why does she have to *keep* coming?

'Maybe she should be asked to call when he's out at Special School. So he won't notice.'

With an effort of will I managed to clear the crockery which Ha had used. Even the windmill mug.

In the bathroom Patti instructed Ha how to clean his own teeth. She teaches him every day. He doesn't seem to learn but she never gives up.

'See Ha's nice new toothbrush, Simon?' she said, in her bright and hopeful voice. 'What colour is it, Ha?'

'Yeah, yeah, lello,' said Ha, squeezing toothpaste along the blue handle. Patti guided his hand.

'No, not yellow, Ha. Look at it carefully. Do you remember? It's blue. We call that colour blue, like the sky.'

The sky was greyish, flecked with darker grey. What kind of teacher was she?

'Boo!' he said.

'Clever boy! That's right. Blue. Isn't he a good boy, doing it all by himself?'

Toothpaste foam dribbled from his mouth. After two brief scrubs he spat everywhere, on the taps, on the cuffs of his pyjamas, some flecks down to his bare feet, the same bare brown feet which had run, shoeless, away from that pit.

'Not finished yet, Ha. Bit more scrubbing round the back.' Patti held her hand over his and gently guided the bristles. 'Rub, rub-a-dub. Must get him slippers. Pity your things won't fit.' I was glad they didn't. I didn't want him wearing my oldest things. 'There's a fine fellow. Isn't he clever?'

'Oh yep. Great. Brillo kid.' I said. Wonder child. Boychild cleans own teeth. Praise be to Allah.

I gave Ha a patronizing pat on the head. If I pretended he was a dog, he seemed pretty good. A dog couldn't clean its own teeth.

'Night,' I said.

'Say good-night to Simon,' said Patti.

'Wanna kish,' said Ha and threw his skinny arms round me and pulled me to him before I had time to escape. He kissed a big, wet, toothpaste-flavoured kiss on my chin. I wiped it off on my sleeve.

'Tell Tony I'll be down in ten minutes,' said Patti. 'Just read Ha a story.'

Now that we were the same age, I supposed we should have gone to bed at the same time. We didn't. Patti always took him up first.

Then we had half an hour round the fire like we always used to, Patti doing her tapestry, me pretending to read an improving novel, and Tony making coffee.

'I was just telling Miss Spaark,' said Patti, as Tony came in with the tray. 'How things are nearly back to normal now.'

Did she really think so? Nothing was ever going to be the same as it used to be. The parents were changed.

Tony always made the coffee, the proper way with filters and fine-ground continental roast, so it tasted French. He'd bring in the tray and I'd have mine with hot milk because milk's full of calcium and other essential nutrients for growing bones. We learned that in Biol., but Patti had already told me.

Now there was only one mug of coffee, instead of three. A mugful of milky coffee just like I always have it. It was the windmill mug and there was a skin on the surface, lapping against the rim where Ha's teeth had clinked. Tony put the tray on a table close to me so I could easily reach it without moving, and he'd put two chocolate digestive biscuits for me as well.

'Aren't you having any?' I said. I took up the mug carefully then put it down again. I wondered how could I drink the coffee without letting my lips touch the rim, without looking at the picture of the windmill?

I wanted to explain to Tony how I really would rather have had any other mug but that one. I wanted to tell them about all the other things I couldn't touch.

But if Tony believed everything could be so easily solved by two chocolate digestive biscuits, how could he possibly understand about the windmill mug, and the rug, and the bannister rail?

I replaced the mug on the tray.

'Patti and I are having something a little stronger tonight,' Tony said, and poured them each a whisky; and they sat, side by side, glumly, tensely clutching their whisky tots. Another difference between then and now. Whisky instead of coffee.

'Is it good for you to drink spirits at night?' I said. We had a talk at school, by the Committee Against Alcoholism, with horrible descriptions of men's rotten livers, and statistics about car accidents caused by drunken drivers.

'Just a nightcap. Your mother's not been sleeping too well. A small whisky's a very acceptable way of unwinding.'

'Better than pills, I suppose. All the same, you ought to watch it. They said so in the talk. You oughtn't to use alcohol as a crutch through difficult times. Children are supposed to report if they're worried about their parents.'

'Simon, with all due respect to your concern for our moral welfare, your mother and I did not need an educational lecture from you as to whether we may drink a whisky nightcap.'

'Sorry,' I said, and kissed them good-night. I left my milky coffee undrunk.

Ha stood at the bathroom basin, wide awake. Cleaning his teeth.

'Ha, you're meant to be in bed! And you've done your teeth already. You don't have to do them twice.'

'Yeah, clean more, more,' he said waving the toothbrush. The red toothbrush. *My* toothbrush. 'Clee tee. Shimoo, clee tee, look me, clee tee. Good boy.'

He opened his mouth wide to show me. I didn't want to see. I snatched back my toothbrush from his monkey hand. 'That's mine! You've used *my* toothbrush. Look red, red, red! Yours is blue. Blue. Like the sky. Mum got you a new toothbrush all your own.' I shook the blue one in his face.

A flicker of a smile across his face. Had he taken mine on purpose or just because he was too stupid to know the difference between old and new, red and blue. 'Look, Ha, *your* toothbrush. D'you see? In future kindly use your own. Now go off to bed. It's late. I'm coming in a moment.'

His face drooped. He glanced at me sideways, then lurched heavily along the passage. I heard the springs squeak, and the plastic mattress cover crackle as he got in. I picked up my toothbrush. He had put it inside his mouth, so I could never use it again. I threw it away in the bin.

He was lying quietly, but not asleep. He was staring at me.

'Don't stare at me like that. Just stop it. Because I don't like it. Just leave me alone. And don't rock tonight.' I don't know why I even bothered to say, don't rock, because he always rocked himself to sleep.

I turned my back on him as I undressed but I knew he was still watching. I didn't know what he was thinking, if he was thinking at all.

I didn't say good-night. I didn't look at him. Even looking at him gave me the creeps.

We didn't have a ladder any more for the bunks. It was up in the attic. I hadn't needed it since I was seven. I used the lower bed as a first step-up. But I could no longer place my bare foot on any part of his bed, not on the mattress, or the rabbit sheets, or the metal frame. With difficulty, I swung myself up, touching no part of his territory, and crawled under my duvet and lay still and straight.

Provided I kept to the narrowest part of my bed, I would be safe. Only the strip down the centre was my own untarnished territory. I was going to keep the light on all night. I was going to stay sitting up all night. I was going to read all night. And when I grew too tired to read, I was going to lie there and think about good things that happened before Ha came.

What happened in the pit was bad. I didn't want to go back to that pit with the crushing weight of bodies.

Ha began to rock himself to sleep. As soon as the bunks started to sway, two men in dirt-green camouflage helmets were standing over me. They grabbed me by the legs and pulled me out of bed. I landed hard on my back.

'He's a gook,' one said. I lay on the contaminated border of the rug, and they seemed to tower over me, with their great black boots, and their rifle butts.

'I've not done anything.' I said. 'Nothing at all.'

'Isn't that exactly the problem? Done sweet nothing.'

'Let me go. It's not me you want. Look, my hair's fair, and my skin. I'm not a gook. It's him you want!' I turned and pointed to Ha, awake and cowering in the lower bunk. I scrambled to my feet and the uniformed men disappeared.

I ran along the passage to their room. The door was half open and their light was out. Yet even through sleep, Patti was usually alert to my presence. Whatever the time of night she would hear me creak along the passage, and I'd hear her voice call from the darkness of their room. 'That you, Simon? You all right, darling?' And I'd whisper back that I was just going for a pee or a drink of water.

Sometimes, in the old days before Ha, she wouldn't call out to me. The bedroom door would be closed. And then I knew that she and Tony were making love and I kept away so they wouldn't hear me and I tried not to hear them. That was the only bad thing about being an only child. I was excluded from love-making and had to go back to my room alone.

It was hard to believe that they'd done that to make me.

I pushed their door more open and looked in. Their bed was flat. They hadn't even come up yet.

I ran downstairs. They were both still side by side, holding their whisky glasses a little more loosely, and a little closer along the sofa than before.

I'd have to tell her about it. She'd always let me talk to her. We'd always been close. I had no secrets from her.

'Hello, Simon,' she said. 'You still awake?'

'Couldn't sleep.' I meant, I didn't want to sleep. 'You see, I've got this worry. A sort of phobia. A kind of obsession thing. About some of the things he does and he makes things happen.'

'What things?'

'Touching things, and, well, you know.' But it seemed too foolish and self-centred to try and explain that where he has touched, I can't go. I can't touch where he has been. There are so many places now. He has even contaminated my sleep.

'You mean, you don't like touching things after he's made them all *messy*?'

'Not that exactly,' I said. Even when he's clean, and scrubbed and powdered like sugared marzipan, I am revulsed by him. 'Well, yes, I suppose that is what I mean.'

'But darling, that's perfectly normal. Nobody likes human mess. Smelly nappies and so on disgust *most* people. Women are supposed to mind less, but only because they've always *had* to care for babies and old people. Honestly, there'd be more wrong with you if you said you *liked* nasty messes!'

She didn't understand. Why should she? She hadn't been where Ha had been. I wanted to tell her about what had happened. But I couldn't get close enough to her any more. I must have imagined a bond between us. I was so different from her. And these days, she was so ugly. Her scraggy hair was pulled back into a messy bunch, and her blotchy face was puffy and tired. I wanted a beautiful mother, a young, feminine mother, with thick shiny hair coiled up in a scarf, and a broad, smooth face with honey-coloured skin. The mother I wanted was at work in the fields, knee-deep in muddy water, a bundle of green seedlings in her right hand, some more in a hessian bag on her back. The seedlings in her hand gleamed a brilliant, caterpillar green, and the sun glanced off the surface of the water casting shafts of silvery light to gleam on her face.

'Patti, am I adopted?' If they'd lied to me about Ha, perhaps they'd lied to me about myself.

'No, of *course* not. What a funny idea. What ever made you think that?' and she reached out and clutched my hand, tight, as though it were a piece of rope, and she was a drowning person in the sea. Then she pulled me down and hugged me.

'Poor darling. It's all so much harder than any of us expected, isn't it? And more frightening in a funny kind of way. Poor us. Poor Ha. Poor you.'

She was a bit drunk. They both were. But the whisky had softened them. She moved closer towards Tony, to make room for me on the cushions beside them.

'What was it like when I was born?' They didn't really want me there, but I didn't want to be left out.

'You? When you were born? It was, oh it was like a miracle, wasn't it darling? We'd waited so long. We were so pleased with you. You were our miracle baby. D'you remember, Tony?'

Tony nodded and smiled, but he was beyond speaking.

'Did you *like* having me?'

'It was fantastic.'

'What time? What time of day was I born?'

'I can't remember. It was just a blur of excitement.'

'Midday,' said Tony, mumbling and genial.

'Champagne, flowers, cards. D'you remember the bottle of champagne, Tony and how it frothed up everywhere and you gave all the nurses a drink in a specimen glass?'

Underneath, Patti mourned a stillborn daughter, and gave all her time to a received son. But I was here first, before the cuckoo in the nest. How could I ever have doubted that I was their firstborn son?

I was so comforted by sitting close to them among the cushions that when I got back to bed, I forgot to stay awake. And I saw a boy lying on his back on the path, gazing up at the sky, legs apart, arms gently out as though resting. Flip-flops on the ground, shorts and a T-shirt. The girl was face down, her head in the grass. All quite silent. Why were their shoes off?

In the distance, blue hills, range upon range of them. Our hills, lovely hills. How can it be so beautiful over there, when these children are lying here in the grass?

Ha began to do strange things. One morning, he decided that he must have his anorak on before he would eat his breakfast. Patti had to get it down from the hook and help him into it. Then, out in town, he suddenly climbed off the push-chair, lay down in the middle of the pavement and began to hum. People thought he was having a convulsion. I knew he wasn't. He was smiling as shoppers stepped round him.

'Don't you mind sometimes? When he's weird and people stare?'

'Of course I mind,' Patti said. 'But I decided, we've got to hold onto him and just do what we can. God gave the normal children the brains to manage on their own. People like Ha haven't got the brains.'

I didn't know she believed in God.

'I don't exactly. I'm not sure. I must admit I didn't know he was going to need our love to go on and on like this. But there we are. I don't think I'd be a real mother if I didn't sacrifice quite a lot for him.'

'But you're *not* his real mother. You're mine.'

'A mother's the person who looks after you and loves you.'

I wish I'd been adopted. It might have been easier. It didn't seem normal them wanting to love somebody who's so bizarre.

'Don't you ever get fed up?'

'Of course. But I just have to get on with it. This is my life. We've received him as a child to be loved. I'll have to do with my life what seems right. You must do with yours whatever *you* think's right. Meanwhile, both of you have our love in different ways.'

For someone who didn't believe in God, she was sometimes too good to be true.

My head was always full of the images that wouldn't go. Babies and trees and dark and light and noise. But I knew now they weren't just dreams or visions. They were so real that I could reach out and feel and see them and hear them, and it was Ha who made them happen.

Babies, trees and noise were easy because they had names. There were other images that I didn't have the words to

131

understand. Shapes and pictures of fear.

When a man, guarding an earth tunnel, steps forward onto a land-mine, hidden in the ground amongst the moss and ferns, pieces of him are thrown about in the air, and the skin of his foot folds back on itself. I fear the unseen eyes of men looking for me. I fear dying.

Perhaps it wasn't Ha that had to be got rid of. It was those things inside my head that had to go.

I had to remain in the forest and avoid people, otherwise I would be shot. I was more afraid of waiting to be found and shot, than of being shot.

So I ran deeper into the trees, scrambling through dense undergrowth, stumbling through wet leaves, clambering over rotting branches slippery with fungi, to where the highlands began. Here, the forest was always misty and damp and the screeching of monkeys in the upper branches of the trees gave way to the repetitive croaking of frogs.

It was colder in the high forest and all night I shivered. Around me I heard the slithering and rustling and twisting of things which move through dank vegetation. I felt insects crawl on me and buzz in my ears, and sting me. I was tired, cold and hungry. I wanted to lie down, but I was afraid even to sit because of scorpions which hide under fallen wood and come out at night to seek their victims.

I shivered and I thought about food. I thought about a meal of rice. When we lived in camp, my mother cooked our rations of rice in the evening when it was dark and there was nothing else to do.

The cooked rice glistened in the black pot. My mother called it pig rice because it was flecked with specks of dirt and husks of straw. It was without salt, and we had no fish sauce. But it looked so good that I was mesmerized by the black pot and the cooked rice.

My mother handed me the chopsticks. We had only one pair left, because so much of our baggage had been mislaid on the journey. I dipped the chopsticks into the small bowl of boiling water to clean them and I passed them to my grandmother. She ate first, but with such slowness, holding the bowl up to her chin, savouring each small mouthful of soft, saltless, flavourless pig rice. Chewing round and round with her toothless gums. She didn't ask for more, though

132

her portion was very small. She finished and she washed the chopsticks in the boiling water and she handed them to my mother to use. My mother gave herself a portion so small you could almost count the number of grains in the bowl. Then it was my turn. And Mai was last of all. She opened up her tiny mouth in readiness for each morsel which my mother gently fed in. Then the cooking pot was empty. The rice had all gone and my grandmother told us about Tu Thuc, the wise young mandarin who travelled far from his own village. From boyhood he had dreamed of discovering the way to the Land of Bliss, where gold and silver fish swim in the lakes, where pastel-coloured clouds are shaped like lotus blossoms, where iridescent petals flutter to the ground like flakes of snow.

At last, Tu Thuc found it. He was welcomed by the Fairy Queen. The Land of Bliss was even better than he had hoped for. Fairy princesses with peach-blossom cheeks, and floating dresses all colours of the rainbow, danced with him. Food was plentiful. The climate was eternal spring. It was a land of youth and pleasure where he spent many days of laughter and happiness. But after a hundred days, despite all the comfort, and all the beauty, he was lonely and missed the simple familiarity of his own home.

The Queen granted his wish to return. But when he got there, all was changed. Nobody recognized him. The people were different. All his relations and contemporaries had long since died. Even his own house was nothing but a dilapidated hut, quite beyond repair. Tu Thuc realized that he had been away from home for one hundred years, for in the Land of Bliss, one single day is worth a whole year on Earth. He was more lonely than ever. Tu Thuc tried to search once more for the Land of Bliss but he had had his chance and he never found it again.

My grandmother always cried when she told the story of Tu Thuc, and my mother always smiled.

But as I sat alone in the highland forest I was angry with myself. I had wanted to think about food. I had ended up thinking about my grandmother, and my mother and my baby sister.

The forest was always full of food, but alone, as a child, with no weapon, I had no way to get it.

There were small, black pigs which a team of men

together could hunt, and shoot with a crossbow, and roast. There were wild bees whose honey was stored in great combs suspended overhead from the upper branches of a tree. There were snakes which men could eat. Once, the men had caught a great boa which was taller than a man when hung on a stick, and which provided a feast of rich meat for everybody in the village.

It was too cold, and too lonely in the upland forest. I heard strange noises and I was afraid. I heard snarling and yelping and I thought they were the cries of the Hungry Spirits from the Other World. They had come to me for offerings of food. I had none to offer. If I gave them nothing they would torment me forever.

When it grew light, I made my way down again through the mist. As my bare legs brushed past the thick leaves, black leeches dropped off the undersides and stuck to my flesh and I had to stop every few paces to pull them off before they sucked all my blood. Instead of finding food, I had become food.

Hunger and fear forced me out from hiding amongst the trees into an open clearing which had once been cultivated. It was a deserted village, with bomb-craters at the centre which had been filled with water long ago and planted with water-growing produce. I pulled out handfuls of watercress and lotus roots and stuffed them into my mouth, just as they were. Then I ran across a stretch of open ground to a small grove of fruit trees on the edge of the village. The mango tree swarmed with sugar ants which had already devoured or pitted most of the fruit. But I found some papaya fruit which were still whole, and cool and juicy.

A small river flowed near the village and staked across the narrowest part was the remains of a fish trap. Most of the wooden lattice and stakes had been washed away but in one place, the trap was still intact. I dipped my hands into the pool and lifted out two small fish and ate them, like the lotus roots, raw.

With enough food inside me to think, I saw that this hamlet, ruined, abandoned half burned-out, was familiar. I had been here before. It was a morning's walk from the village where we used to live. So now I was safe. I knew which direction to go to find my father.

When I woke and smelled the bacon frying and toast browning, it occurred to me with a jolt of surprise, that I had never, in my whole life, been hungry. I had never felt a need for food which makes your stomach ache, not just with greed and longing, but with real pain. Hunger which makes your stomach swell, and your hair fall out, and your teeth loose in your head, and your limbs shrivel.

I remembered the photo in the beige file downstairs, of Ha with no hair and his legs like chicken bones with all the flesh picked off, and his eyes like burned currants.

Three meals a day, three square meals as my mother called them, sometimes even four, had always been provided.

'Sorry, Ha. I got it wrong again.' I gave him both my rashers at breakfast and ate only toast without butter or marmalade.

When I reached the long, straight path between the orchards, I was alert for the louts. I peered at every leaf to see if it twitched, to see if their eyes were darting behind the green. I saw faces, which disappeared. Then I didn't see them. The sides of the hedges were so tall that they nearly met overhead in a thick green canopy which shut out the light, so that only grey-green twilight filtered down to the ground. The drizzling air was warm and smelled of rotting compost. As my bare hands brushed past the damp grass, insects flicked onto me. Plant life grew through the hedge abundantly, vines and shoots and tendrils locked together nearly strangling each other, trying to reach away from the green shadows and up to find the light.

In the school library, there was a book called *The World of Weapons*. I read it in the lunch hour.

> The Bouncing Betty, a common mine, and greatly feared by jungle patrols, leaps from its nest on earth when the initial charge sends the device on a one-metre, vertical leap. On reaching its apex, it explodes. Bouncing Betty is one of the less destructive devices, usually claiming no more than one, or sometimes two victims. Where the mine is in an old emplacement, and has been exposed to the rains, the three prongs which serve as The Bouncing Betty's firing device, may be seen jutting out of the earth, and the mine can be avoided.

I found my father alone, guarding an ammunition cache which was disguised with clumps of bamboo carefully planted to seem natural. I called very softly to him through the green. I didn't know, at first, if he was alone. I didn't know if anybody else was there. He turned his head quickly, looking all round. His rifle was aimed towards me. I thought he was going to shoot me, either on purpose or by mistake. Then he saw me, recognized who I was, and I came running out from hiding and pushed my way towards him.

On the path in front of me, there were three crossed sticks warning me. But I forgot about the warnings and hurried to my father with my arms outstretched. Like the mandarin, Tu Thuc, who wanted to find his way back home to the people he knew, I was compelled to go to my father.

But he wasn't smiling. He didn't want me.

'No! Ha!' he called. 'Stay over there! Don't come here. Wait.'

But I didn't wait. I went on running to him because he was the last person left. He came forward to stop me and it wasn't me, but my father, who triggered the booby trap which he had carefully hidden, and set in the path.

A patrol of five U.S. infantrymen discovered me. I was still with my father's body. By now it was moving with white ants. They didn't know what to do with me. They made me squat on the ground with my hands on my head.

'Take him prisoner? You fooling? Then we gotta give him bed, blanket, pillow, three meals a day, so many cubic metres of personal space. We got Geneva people on our backs.'

'Our directive is systematic elimination, not prisoners.'

'Anyhow, he's too young to be trouble. He couldn't be — what — more'an seven or eight years old at most.'

'These gooks always look younger than they are. We got a VC yesterday, looks about fourteen. Just a kid. His ID we found on him says he's thirty-one! Can you believe that? He looks like he's not even out of High School, and he's ten years older than me.'

'It's their diet. Keeps them short. Stunted.'

Four of the men settled themselves comfortably down and lit up cigarettes. The fifth stood nearby on guard with his weapon up all the time. They weren't, after all, afraid that I might run for it, but feared something else.

'Have you seen inside their hooches? We fired one, the other week. VC stronghold. Burned it right down. You should see how they live. It's just something else. They got no light, only those paraffin lamps. No drugs. They don't even know aspirin. They're all half sick with TB and skin disease by the look of them.'

One of the others nodded. 'Yep, all they want is a bit of rice to eat. That's all they need to keep them happy.'

'They're like animals sometimes. Eating nothing but rice. Their whole life, it's food and reproduction, and if they're lucky a bit of land for growing things. That's all. No running water in their homes, no gas, no electrics, no *ambition*.'

One of the others who hadn't joined in, said, 'You know, Cap'n, I figure we're going about this war the wrong way. I figure how as we could do it different. With a good steak dinner. If we was to give all these jungle people a nice steak, we'd be more like to sort of convince them.'

One of the others punched him in the ribs.

'Steak dinner! Don't you say that. I can't stand that talk.'

'Oh yeah, steak dinner, big T-bone, stretching right across the plate, this big.' He held out his arms wide. 'Fried in butter, pile of french fries, crispy, hot. Lots of relish.'

'Chilli relish.'

'Yeah, and dill pickle. And two cans of Budweiser.'

'Followed up by a big apple pie, and cream.'

'Bilberry.'

'OK, bilberry.'

Thinking about food made them hungry. They decided to eat their rations. Each had cans of food in their packs, meat, and fruit in juice, and hard biscuits. They opened the cans and ate the food with their knives.

'Geeze, this is bad!' said one, and he exchanged his tin of meat with another man's tin of fruit.

One of them threw his empty can to the ground. The other kicked it further into the undergrowth and told him to get on with it.

'You goddam frisby! Don't you know nothing yet? You don't leave it there where them gooks can find it. You take it with you. OK?'

The one who had dropped his can crawled around the ground on his hands and knees till he'd found it. He put it in his pack.

I was still sitting with my hands on my head, when they decided it was time to move on.

'We gonna interrogate this kid or not?'

They decided they would. Then they could report back on the radio how they had made contact with the enemy, if I was the enemy. 'Cap'n'll like that.'

I didn't want to be the enemy. When they started to question me, I knew what sort of answers to give.

'VC number ten,' I said in their language, and pointed with one hand, over to where my father lay, keeping my other hand on my head. 'VC number ten. US number one.' I pointed to myself. 'I US number one. No number ten.'

The man who'd thrown his can away and had to retrieve it, said, 'What's that kid saying? What's he mean by that jibber jabber?'

'It's their way of speaking. Kind of metaphor. Number ten, that means bad to them. They don't have no other words to say it. They don't have words like good and bad. They say ten is bad, and number one is good. Sort of pidgin talk.'

'Don't they have nothing in between?'

'I don't know. I guess so. But I ain't never heard them say it.'

They didn't have an interpreter, so they had to go on with the questioning in the same way.

'VC you village? Where VC? You father VC? You mother VC?'

'I no village VC. I village number ten. No VC. You US number one. I number one you.'

So they gave me the leftovers of food from the cans. I had been warned many times in the past against eating any food which they offered in case it was poisoned. But hunger changes one's fears. Then they took me along with them. I had no one else to go with. I carried one of their packs.

We spent the night in a foxhole filled with ants, and they shared their C-rations with me again. In the foxhole one of them was awake on guard while the other four were supposed to sleep. But nobody slept. They were constantly alert for any sound that might be an ambush. But there was nobody out there. Nobody attacked them.

'We're on a fool's errand. Not a peep out of Charlie all night.'

'Maybe he's lying low?'

'Maybe he doesn't know we're here?'

'Maybe he's not out there at all?'

'Charlie Six. This is Charlie Two. All secure. Situation remains the same. Proceeding to rendezvous Green Lady.'

They were trying to reach some pre-arranged place, following orders on a piece of paper, and every so often checking with their headquarters on the radio. When we were going through the forest, they always travelled in single file, keeping at a distance of five paces from the man ahead. They took it in turns to be point man and break trail because being leader was the most dangerous place. Being last was dangerous too because of snipers at your back. They wore green trousers tucked into the tops of their jungle boots as protection against sharp grasses and spiking seedheads which whipped against your legs.

Sometimes it was hard for me to keep up with them. They were tall, and their strides were so much longer than mine. One of them wanted to get rid of me.

'Don't fraternize with the kids. You know we been told that.'

He thought I was an enemy decoy, sent to lead them astray or send out signals. But the others said I should stay. I was like their lucky mascot. They hadn't made contact with the enemy since I'd been with them. So I stayed.

They were brave men in their way. They were very frightened, but they went headlong towards their fear. They took a direct line through any obstacle in their way.

Where there was open ground to be crossed with nowhere except a thorn bush to hide, the men didn't look for a safe way round but ran straight across, one at a time, while the others kept their rifles ready.

They waded, one by one, waist-deep through a swamp of dark-red mud, rotten smelling, and so deep that I would have drowned in it. But one of them, already weighted down by his huge pack, carried me sitting on top of the pack, so that he sunk even deeper than the others. I held his rifle in my hands above my head to keep it out of the water.

Dragonflies zigzagged backwards and forwards low over the murky surface of the swamp. There were always dragonflies before the rains came. When we were across, and up on to firmer ground, my carrier had great leeches as big as a man's toe, clinging to his legs, and he burned them off with a lighted cigarette.

Late on the second day we reached the place they wanted, still without having seen or heard anybody to shoot at. It was level ground between some scrubby trees and low bushes. They waited behind the trees and one of them took a grenade from his belt, unpinned it, and threw it into the centre of the clearing. Thick yellow smoke oozed out from the container. It was a signal of some sort, for they all waited anxiously without speaking. The sky was thick and overcast, and the air felt heavy, pressing in on us from all sides. Even the insects usually chirruping in the grass, were quiet.

Then I heard the chugging of a motor overhead and knew what they were waiting for. A small helicopter was overhead, its rotating wings sending a downwind to flatten the long, sharp grasses. As soon as the men heard it, they grinned with relief and self-congratulation. They relaxed. They forgot about running in single file and keeping a safe distance from one another. They ran together in a happy cheering bunch towards where the helicopter was coming down in the open.

But, just as it had nearly reached the ground, a sudden burst of firing came from the trees opposite. All around the helicopter was alive with exploding shells, the noise echoed and re-echoed against the trunks of the trees.

'Holy Moses! Red hot LZ!' one of the men shrieked. All five flung themselves back for cover while the helicopter lurched awkwardly into the sky again, then rose up and away.

The man who worked the radio pack began screaming into the receiver.

'Charlie One to Charlie Six, Landing Zone hot. We're taking fire. Incoming? Of course it's incoming. No, I don't give a rat's ass. Just get them back on down and get us the hell out of here. And double quick time or it's purple heart time for five stiff grunts.'

The other four fired repeatedly towards the clump of trees on the far side though there was nothing and nobody to be seen. But when the helicopter returned the pounding of shells began again. This time, there was a gunner crouched at the open side of the helicopter firing towards the trees. The machine-gun fire rattled down like small stones off the leaves.

The helicopter came down to hover just above ground level, but without touching it. Like dragonflies over the water, its wings seemed too slight for the weight of the body. One at a time, the five men from my patrol ran, bent-up double, beneath the whirling blades, while the others yelled at them with terror and encouragement. Arms reached out and each was hauled aboard. All the time the machine-gunner at the door went on firing into the trees. When the last man was still only half-in, gripped from above but his legs hanging helpless in space, the helicopter lifted up and away.

I sat and watched it until it was only a speck in the heavy sky, out of sight, and out of hearing. I had mishandled the rescue. If I'd run with them, and held up my arms to be pulled aboard, they'd probably have taken me with them.

There was nobody here now. Whoever had been behind the trees didn't wait for me either.

2

Some mornings in assembly, as well as normal announcements about abuse of showers, and changes in the dinner timetable, the Head gave us talks on matters of national importance.

'War,' he told us, 'is sometimes a necessary evil. Which had,' he paused to adjust his gown where it hung from his shoulders. 'Most reluctantly,' he paused to straighten the lectern in front of him. 'To be waged against fascists, dictators and other bully-boys who are inclined to stamp over smaller nations. Now, I prefer to keep politics out of school life. Out.'

Rows of boys in assembly listened, or did not listen, to Fisher's morning chat. Informing us that war is sometimes a necessary evil.

'We are, here, in this school, as you all know, running a non-political ship. Education is essentially an apolitical matter. So there will be *no* political issues argued in this school.'

We knew. Already, no boy was allowed to display any badge on his blazer lapel, no boy allowed to pin up any poster, nor canvass for any cause however noble, without permission from the Head. And permission was never granted for any cause which could be called political or inflammatory. It was the Head's decision what counted as political or inflammatory.

'Now, idealism is all very well. However, it can be misplaced and it is perfectly clear to me, that this new "Freedom Group for Youth" or whatever it calls itself, is particularly obnoxious in its clandestine political propaganda.' Fisher's face was growing red as he warmed to the theme. It was an inflammatory matter.

Gradually, we began to realize what he was driving at. 'And it is insidious that older members of school should have used their positions of authority to disseminate their own woolly-headed views amongst the youngest and most susceptible boys.'

Now we knew exactly what he was on about. Several boys at the front of the hall shifted anxiously on their chairs. Some of the sixth formers were doing Peace Studies for A levels. There'd been a secret Peace Group forming amongst them, though since most of the boys knew about it, it was more of a not-so-secret group. Winston Pelham was part of it.

In the dinner hour they'd put on a play behind the bike-sheds. The bike-sheds are where people usually go to smoke, so there was a spot of anti-peace between smokers and peace activists before the play even began. Frankly, the show was a bit amateurish I thought. But you could see that they were trying to say something which they thought was important.

It was about what happened to a family in Hiroshima after the bomb. Winston played a Japanese housewife in her paper-walled home. A couple of other sixth-formers were supposed to be her tiny Japanese children who were burned up in the scorching rays of the instant sunshine.

It was embarrassing almost, to see these huge boys shuffling around with coloured crêpe-paper sashes over their grey woollen blazers, and talking in high sing-song voices pretending to be child-Japs. But nobody laughed.

Then, the show had just got to the didactic bit, spouting statistics at us, about how there'd been a hundred and seventy-eight full-scale wars since The War which is the only one most people think of, and how the world governments spent a million, trillion, zillion dollars a year on armaments which could be spent on food, when a junior master came on it. All the staff know perfectly well that behind the bike-sheds is where boys go to smoke, and so usually they keep well away. But this one must have been warned to come and interfere. Somebody must have told him.

And as a result the following morning in assembly, we had to endure Fisher's chat.

'So, those older boys who were principally involved, have already been rebuked. But there may be others among you, whose part in the charade has not come to light. We are not going to have a witch-hunt, but I will take this opportunity to put right a few details which may have slipped your notice.'

It was beginning to sound as though we were in for one of his massive three-quarters of an hour monster talks when you end up missing first period. Boys settled themselves more comfortably on their chairs. Heads drooped, shoulders relaxed.

'So, peace between East and West,' Fisher's voice droned on.

'And, of crucial importance.

The younger generations in our society are given.

A safe, a true, and a democratic world.

In which to grow. Security of the free world can be achieved by many means including adequate defence.'

If you didn't concentrate too hard, you could let it all wash gently over you.

143

'And maintain the balance of power.

Sometimes, that defence must extend beyond the boundaries of our own territories.

And as Head of this school.

Member of the association of Headmasters.'

I. I. I. Me. Me. Me. He loved talking about himself. Soon, he'd begin reminiscing about his days at school when boys really were boys.

'Must fully support the work of the British Atlantic Committee.

Twin goals of defence and *détente*.'

Soon, he got on to one of his favourite topics.

'World Communism.'

Sometimes, it was the march of Communism, sometimes the creeping scourge of Communism. Today, it was the heavy boot of Communism stamping on people like ourselves.

'The people of those countries are *terrified*! Every moment in terror of their lives! And so that is what it is all about.'

His voice was getting louder all the time, booming through the hall so that you couldn't help listening even if you tried not to.

'Is there CND in Russia? I should like you boys to ask yourselves that one question! Ask yourselves, too, if the Russkies came here, what would they do first? Would they rush round to the back of the bike-sheds and listen to your pathetic little message? I rather think not!

The heavy boot is crushing the small nations, with unthinking brutality.

Which is why war must, sometimes, be a necessary evil.'

How could it be necessary? War crushed too, just as much as the big C. Was killing ever really necessary? Didn't he *know* that war killed people? Not just soldiers, but women, and old men, and buffaloes and babies. And when it didn't kill them, it blew their legs off and their minds out. And when war didn't hurt them with bombs or bullets, it did it by starvation and deprivation. And even when it didn't starve them, war destroyed people's traditions, and their trust for one another, and their ancestors' tombs. How could he talk to us as though he knew *everything*, when he didn't even know these simple facts?

I shut my eyes so that I wouldn't see his mouth moving. But his voice was insistent.

'Without adequate deterrent. Which must even be aggressive.'

I tried to hum.

'They would be *all* over us! Just like they were all over Hungary, Romania, Albania. Freedom, true freedom, is what it is all about!'

I counted to myself. His words infiltrated my ears. I put my fingers in my ears. His words crept past my fingers.

Then he began to roar about God. We had finally reached his religious message and I decided I had had enough. I got up and edged along the row, past the twenty pairs of ink-stained hands, the twenty pairs of grey terylene knees, tripping over twenty pairs of size six feet. Several boys stared at me and grinned.

'Please stand now, School.'

A thousand boys shuffled sleepily to an upright position. By the time I was making my own way down the aisle to the door at the back of the hall, a thousand boys were singing about fighting the good fight with all their might. But what *was* a good fight? How could you tell?

Then, a thousand boys must pray for right to triumph. But which right? How do you recognize the right side when you see it?

The staff sit in a row at the back and snooze. I was quickly past them and out through the swing-doors. They closed behind with a thud. A master watched me leave. He followed me out. In the corridor, he came over to me and touched my shoulder.

'Feeling faint?'

'No, sir.'

'You all right?'

'Yes, sir.'

'What's up?'

'Didn't like what he was saying, sir. It seems he wants us to pray for wars. How can he say that. What does *he* know about wars? He doesn't know a thing. He's entitled to his opinions, sir, but that's no reason why I should have to have his opinions stuffed down my throat and then pray about them.'

'Your parents Quakers?'

'No, sir. They're agnostics, I think. My mother sometimes says she's a very lapsed Catholic.'

'Just wondered. What about you?'

'Buddhist, sir. Maybe. Not sure, but either way, I can't really pray about wars.'

'You CND?'

'No, sir. Never join anything. Safer not to.'

Fisher's prayer was coming to an end. We could hear the

fellowship of the Holy Spirit seeping out through the closed doors.

'Very well. Fair enough. You'd better slip along to your form room and wait there quietly till the rest of them are out.'

'Thank you, sir. By the way, I think he's a hypocrite too, he says he doesn't approve of indoctrination of younger boys by older boys, then he goes and indoctrinates the whole school. But he hasn't managed to indoctrinate *me*! I *know* about war. More than he does anyway. And I'd rather not stand there praying about it. I don't go a bundle on praying, even at the best of times.'

'Which form are you? Why not have a word with your RE teacher, about your feelings.'

'It's not a question of feelings, sir. It's a question of *facts*.' My voice — like Fisher's — seemed to be getting louder.

There was a scraping of chair-legs in the hall. Assembly was over. The double doors swung open. Boys streamed out. And then Fisher blew out on the wide black wings of his gown.

He strode up. 'I'll see about this,' he said, and the master, dismissed, slid away into the stream of boys.

'Well, what's your name, boy?' the Head asked.

I told him.

'And I suppose that noisy exit from assembly was intended as some kind of infantile protest?'

'No, sir. Not exactly, sir. You see, sir. In my opinion —'

'Boys in second year don't have opinions. Not here they don't up till fifth year, it's facts you're here for. I've never liked you much. To be honest, I've hardly even *noticed* you, since you started here. You have a sly manner of keeping yourself out of sight. What they call a low profile. And you contribute very little to the community of the school. You've never had anything to say for yourself. But now that you have chosen, in this insolent way, to make yourself noticeable, I can see that my earlier judgement was probably correct. You are not a particularly likeable boy. Now, perhaps you would go along to my office and wait for me there.'

I went, and I waited. I didn't know how long I had to wait, nor what he was going to say. Or whether I was supposed to stand or sit while I waited. I didn't know what he was going to do to me when he came. I didn't know if he was going to question me. And if he did, I didn't know what I was meant to say. I didn't know what the right answers were, or the wrong answers.

Why is Communism wrong?

I don't know, sir.

Why is military brutality right?

I don't know.

Why is war normal, and necessary?

I don't know.

Why is it expedient to massacre?

I don't know.

Do you know what happens when a man stands on a land-mine?

No.

Do you know what happens when a body bursts open?

No.

Do you know why children are starving?

Do you know why I feel sick? Do you know why I must get away from here? Do you know why I must lose myself?

> I wandered away from where the ambush had happened. I was hungry. The night we spent in the foxhole, one of the patrol had given me a bar of pink soap which he carved into the shape of an eagle for me. I took it from my pocket and tried to eat it. I had nothing else.
>
> Then I came to an old woman by the side of a road, winnowing rice in a shallow basket. She was small and bent over her work, and for a moment I was sure she was my grandmother till I remembered we'd left my grandmother behind.
>
> I spoke to her. I offered her the carved soap in exchange for some rice. But she wouldn't answer me. She ignored me. She went on tossing the rice in the basket, as though I wasn't even there. She was oblivious to everything. Didn't she know there was a war going on around her, and men trying to kill each other? Hadn't she heard the noise of the ambush?
>
> I sat down on the dirt road, and that was the end. I died. I never lived again. There was no way back to the Land of Bliss.

What happened after that? Something must have.

I can't remember.

You must remember. I have to know. You didn't stay sitting on the road forever. Listen, Ha, I can't keep on making this up for myself. Your story's more important than mine. I want your

147

story. Show me what happened. I left the Head's office without waiting for him to turn up. But I didn't know where to go next. I'd sometimes wondered what I'd do if I bunked off school. Before, I'd supposed I could go home. Home was the haven, the nest, the security, the primeval cave. The lair which every bear needs. But now, no cave. It wasn't my cave any more. It was Ha's.

After the cat, I'd thought to rid our family of Ha. I'd failed. I'd got it all wrong. It wasn't Ha who had to be got rid of. It was myself who had to go. It was me who didn't belong, who had caused all the trouble, who hated and resented. He had sufffered, while I had just lived, and used, and taken.

Murderers and convicts on the run can take refuge in churches. Sacred ground is safe ground. So I jogged through the orchards, across the housing estate and down into town, and I found myself a church, the first church I came to, a fourteenth century city church tucked away behind a cinema and a greengrocer's shop.

An old man was cutting grass round the graves, bent over his work.

'Excuse me,' I said. He didn't answer me. He went on at the grass and didn't even turn round. 'Excuse me, please.'

I wanted to take refuge in his church and he didn't bother to speak to me.

It wasn't till he straightened up that I saw his face, and then I realized there was something wrong with him. He made a strange, guttural noise which wasn't speaking. He sounded like the children on Ha's school bus. He waved his hands towards the porch of the church, and made more strange noises at me.

So I went in.

Patti and Tony don't go to church. Patti used to. But not any more. Because they never took me, I wasn't sure what to do. I know what they do in films. An actor, dressed in robes like a priest, mounts the pulpit and delivers an angry sermon. An actress, with a black lace veil over her head, slides serenely into a black pew, kneels and raises her eyes to the vaulted ceiling. That was only films. I knew it didn't happen like that in real churches.

I closed the creaking wooden door behind me softly, so as not to disturb the group of people having a service at the front of the church. They were very silent. They made almost no sound. In films, there's music. Here, there was none. The word wasn't spoken. I knelt down at the back and quickly closed my eyes so that I should look as though I was praying.

They seemed to pray for a long time. I opened my eyes. The other group were no longer kneeling. Now, they were sitting. Still no word spoken, because they were doing it all with their hands, even the priest, in sign language with grimaces and occasional grunts.

I realized what I'd done. I'd come to a special church for dappy people. They were all dum-dums and they all understood what was going on while I was left out.

Then, one of the women noticed me, crept from her pew and came back to me with her hand out to me, smiling a terrible smile. She had crooked eyes and thick glasses and she said something to me in a strange, croaking voice like the gardener outside. I couldn't understand.

She said it again, doing her hand-talking at the same time. She was trying to tell me something. At last, I made her out. She was trying to tell me that they were having their Ascension Day Service and would I like to join them at the front?

I left the church quickly. It was no refuge for me. I didn't belong anywhere. Even the dum-dums had a place in church. I was a bright High School boy who had no place at all.

I wished I was dead, then it would all be so much easier for everybody. I left the church and ran through the middle of town, and out towards the ring road. Above the moving blur of traffic hung an intoxicating cloud of petrol fumes, the magic smell of war.

Stepping onto the ring road was like entering a deep, swift stream with currents of moving water rushing by on either side. I was half-way across and still nothing touched me. I walked steadily on. Something would have to get me soon. I was nearly to the other side.

Then, in the far lane, I saw my last chance: a red saloon car. I threw myself into the empty space on the greasy surface of the road, just before the wheels. It hit me, but it didn't kill me. I fell forward on to the grass verge, clutching my head and rocking backwards and forwards to ease the pain.

A ragged procession made its way along a road. Refugees pushed their possessions in overloaded handcarts, or carried them in baskets slung on their shoulders. There were some old men and wounded young in the group, but mostly women and children.

I watched them pass and I didn't know where they were

going to. I wanted to follow but I was too tired for walking so I rolled further into the ditch.

Get up, Ha! You can't just lie in the ditch. You've got to keep moving.
Why?
Because that's what refugees have to do.
What's a refugee?
A refugee is an unwanted person who makes claims on the humanity of others without having anything to give in return. Nobody wants your scrap of Lifebuoy soap.

Later, I heard the creak of wooden wheels, the jolting of a vehicle. I crawled up from the ditch and against the sky I saw the curved crescent shape of a pair of buffalo horns. I ran out onto the road. The buffalo cart trundled slowly forwards, with only one man on it, and four baskets of fruit at the back. The old man was slumped underneath his straw hat, half asleep. I waved at him, and he grunted that I was free to climb on the back if I wanted.

We overtook the group of walkers. They were people trying to escape the fighting in their village by going towards the city. The old man said,

'It won't make any difference where they go. We're all like flies caught in a trap. It's America and China's war, and Russia's. Not ours. The people of the South get killed, the same for the men from the North. But we're all the same people, or we would be if we could be left in peace. It's all gone on too long. Soon, it'll be impossible for anybody to recover.'

When we reached the city, there were more crowds than I had ever seen before. The buildings were tall, with shutters, and glass in the windows. The streets were wide, and paved so that the wooden wheels of the cart turned smoothly. The roads were lined with red-flowering flame-trees casting shade on the passers-by below. Lingering in the air were the smells of flowers from the market and of cooking food.

In some places, the road was blocked with convoys of lorries, with taxis, and pedicabs, motor-scooters, and bicycles. People darted between the traffic to cross the road. There was a haze of petrol fumes and a noise of motor engines, and brakes squealing, and horns and klaxons. We saw no other buffalo carts in the city. Our cart, moving so slowly, added to the congestion until a policeman blew a shrill whistle at the old man and told him he was to hurry on out of the way.

Although there were military trucks on the road, and soldiers on the pavements, there seemed to be no war here. The soldiers weren't shelling the buildings, or firing on the crowds. The people, richly dressed, laughed and chatted as they walked along, and didn't seem afraid.

As the cart passed down into a narrow alley, three urchins darted out in front of the buffalo's hoofs, distracting the old man. Another boy ran round to the back of the cart where I was lying, and pulled off one of the baskets of limes so quickly and deftly that I hardly saw what was happening.

I should have tried to stop him but my body felt too languid to move. All four boys disappeared into the crowds.

'Thieves!' the old man muttered. 'A city of robbers and corruption. They're out to break us on every side.'

Further along, two soldiers stopped him. They wanted to see his market permit and to search the cart for arms. I was afraid they wanted to question me too and I had forgotten what the correct answers were. I slid off the cart and tried to lose myself in the surge of people on the pavement who jostled and pushed this way and that.

Among the rich were shoeshine boys and boom-boom girls, pickpockets, traders and hawkers. One-legged beggars and no-legged beggars, and greedy, wild children who shoved and scratched at each other and clamoured at strangers for sweets and gum. A boy grabbed at my pocket to see if I had any money. All he found was the piece of pink soap carved like an eagle, but he took it.

Traders sold pressed-fruit drinks, and fried morsels of catfish, and noodle soup. They were in competition with one another. One attracted custom with a wooden rattle which he shook. One had a little brass bell. Another shouted out to passers-by. I stared at the cups of hot noodle soup. The smell was good, but the man told me to go away. I was distracting customers.

Then at dusk, quite suddenly the streets emptied. The crowds disappeared. The traffic dissolved. Soon, there were only military police in jeeps, patrolling the roads, and all that remained on the pavements were deserted stalls, piles of rubbish and children with nowhere to go.

The city wasn't the Land of Bliss. The paved roads were too wide. There was nowhere to hide. The bright red trees were planted too far apart to offer any kind of shelter. And from far away, I heard the low thumping of bombing and I knew that, after all, there was still a war.

On a pile of garbage, I found a cardboard packing-case and I crawled into it and went to sleep.

The rounded edge of the metal car bumper rammed into my leg and knocked me forward on to the grass verge. As I fell, I hit the back of my head on the kerb and my glasses shot off. I screamed and screamed. It didn't hurt, but I screamed as loudly as I could and I went on falling backwards with the sky swirling round and round overhead, the trees upside down rotating, and helicopters coming over the horizon in formation, bobbing like green ducks, swimming upside down through the air.

The traffic roared past. It was so noisy that nobody could hear me scream. I wondered if I was going to die. But I knew I couldn't die. I was going to be forced to live for as long as Ha lived, just the same, on and on. Then a man towered above me like a dark mountain against the sky.

'I could've killed you!' he shouted angrily. 'You silly young fool! What the heck d'you think you're playing at?' I watched his mouth like a huge crater opening and shutting as he roared. 'Running right in front like that! You could've caused a serious accident. All the other cars behind! They might've piled right into us. Why can't you boys use the subway? What d'you think it's there for?'

I staggered to my feet, swaying slightly. My shin hurt where the bumper had rammed into it. I clutched hold of my leg and squeezed it, rocking backwards and forwards to ease the pain.

'You hurt?' he asked more gently. His car was half-way up on the kerb and the driver's door was swinging open.

'No,' I said. 'I'm all right.'

'Did my car touch you? I felt something.'

'Just my leg. Bruised. That's all.'

'You ought to go to Casualty. In case. I'd better take you. What's your name? You practically passed out. You might be more hurt than you think.' He ran round his car, and reached through to unlock the near-side door, then he came to help me in.

152

I pushed him off.

'Look, it was my fault,' I snapped. 'You said so. And I admit it. And I'm all right. I'm sorry. Is that enough?'

I picked up my blazer and my glasses and limped away from him towards the pedestrian subway.

'But listen, lad, if you're injured — ' He started to follow me, but then paused. His car was an obstruction in the main road and the traffic was having to brake and swerve round it.

'I'm all right, I told you, and I apologize for causing trouble.'

'Look, take my address,' he called after me.

'It's not normal to admit liability. Your insurance company wouldn't like it. Leave me alone,' and I hobbled down into the subway. He couldn't follow me with his car down there. When I came up the other side, his car had gone and the traffic was flowing smoothly again.

I'd tried to kill myself on the ring road. But all I'd managed to do was make one man frightened and angry. Anyway, I knew now I wasn't going to be able to die till Ha died, and Ha was protected by the spirits of his ancestors.

Two young women woke me from my cardboard box. They were round-eyes, and they were in some kind of uniform, but they weren't soldiers. They peered down at me in my box, their white faces like moons against the sky.

Like soldiers, they interrogated me, but differently. No 'Where VC? You VC?' Instead, they asked, 'Where is your father? Where is your mother? Your family all dead? Where are your ancestors buried?'

When I said nothing, they helped me out of the cardboard carton and took me. They had a pick-up van full of other children. They had amputees, retards, fools, cretins, and wounded.

I didn't know who these women were, or where they were taking us, or why. I went with them from fear. Fear of the unknown future couldn't be as bad as fear of the past.

An unfamiliar red car was parked outside our house. It was the one I'd walked into.

They were all there, a great crowd of them in the kitchen. Miss Spaark, and Patti and Tony, and the man from the ring road. Then Ha's minibus pulled up in the street and he lurched in on the arm of the bus-escort, adding to the confusion of people

153

cluttering up my home just when I wanted peace and quiet.

I knew it'd be like this. Questions. All talking at once.

'Simon!'

'Yes, that's the boy. I recognize him. And the blazer. I knew that uniform as soon as I saw it!'

'Where on *earth* have you been?'

'In church. Thinking.'

The phone rang. One more person wanting to come and interfere. Ha, beside me, jiggered up and down, pulling at my sleeve, grabbing at my school-bag.

Patti held out the phone to Tony. 'It's Fisher. For you.'

'Who?' said Tony.

'Fisher. From the school. He says the accident on the ring road was reported to him.'

'That was *me*!' said the man. 'I knew the grey blazer. *I* reported it.'

'And he says Simon's hardly been there all week.'

Hadn't I? That was odd. I thought I had.

The fluorescent lighting along the ceiling jumped and danced, yellow and white like stars. I looked at the crowd of staring faces. Tony looked at me as though I came from another world.

'An accident?' he said. 'What sort of accident?'

'Explosion.'

'Where?'

'On the outskirts of the city. At the ammunition depot. They think it was an insurgent. Probably been working there for months as a gate-guard.'

'Security's hardly their strong point! What's the casualty rate?'

'A dozen. They're not too concerned about that. It's the loss of armaments they're worried about. Thank goodness this isn't nuclear, or we'd all be frying.'

The sky was lit with a golden glow. A spray of brilliant silver sparkles was followed by a succession of heavy thuds, as one tank after another went off. But there was no ammo depot on the edge of our city. I must have got it wrong. We live in a safe corner of the south-east. Yet the brilliant sparkles were definitely there. The silver light zigzagged right through my eyes so I was half-blinded.

'What's the matter, Simon?'

'You've had us all so desperately worried. What *is* going on?'

I heard their far-off voices, and their concern.

'Tony!' I screamed. 'I can't see! I'm blind! Help me!'

There was a noise inside my head and the pain was intense. He led me up to my room and laid me down with great gentleness. How could I have believed that my father didn't love me? He closed the curtains.

'Tony, I feel so ill. I think I'm going to die. I think I'm going to be sick.'

I heard him find clean pyjamas in my drawer. I felt, rather than saw, him changing me.

Ha stood and watched. I couldn't see him because of the flashing lights, but I knew that he was there.

'Yeah, yeah, yeah, yeah. Shimoo sick, sick, sicky. Yucky, yucky, yucky, yucky. Agh.'

I almost laughed, but the pain inside my head was too great.

'That's enough now, Ha,' Tony said quietly. 'Don't tease him when he's not well.'

There was a continual thudding in the background, keeping time with the flashing lights and with the blood coursing through my veins.

Later, Patti came up. She was less calming than Tony. She talked. She tweaked at the curtains. She straightened my duvet. She stroked my head, and made loud footsteps that echoed through my skull, but at least she told me what was wrong.

'It's a migraine, Simon darling. That's all.'

'I'm blind,' I said.

'Not really. It's only a very bad headache. You'll be all right by tomorrow. What Granny used to call a sick headache.'

Headache? This was no headache. I could feel my whole head coming off.

'You've probably inherited it from her. I expect it's all the stress.'

I wish she'd stop talking. At least Tony kept quiet. The talking hurt as much as the light coming through a chink in the curtains where she'd tweaked them open.

'It could be caused by any number of things. Allergy to oranges. Did we have oranges today? Some people say chocolate. Or low blood sugar. You probably didn't eat any lunch today, did you? Or maybe delayed concussion from the accident.'

It wasn't an accident. It was an incident. And I wish she'd stop talking.

'It can be connected with high blood pressure, building up

155

under the cranium, producing a pressure on the soft tissues, just beneath the bone.'

Tony came in. 'Pattie darling,' he said gently. 'I shouldn't give him the full medical lecture now. Let's just see what we can do to make him comfortable and find the causes later.'

They were worried. I could tell by the way doors closed silently as I came gingerly downstairs. By the way they talked in lowered tones and broke off in mid-sentence when I came in.

For once it was me, not Ha, who was on their minds.

Patti went on calling it migraine and I was taken to the doctor's surgery to see if her diagnosis was correct.

No brain tumour. No high blood pressure. Heart still beating. Eyes in order, due for a re-test next year.

The G.P. asked, 'Simon, is there, in your own opinion, anything in particular, do you think, which might have triggered this off?'

Yes, as a matter of fact, doctor, I think I'm turning into my brother.

Well, he's not my brother. He's the foster child my parents got, and I'm not actually turning *into* him. That's an exaggeration. It's more that I tend to *think* about him an awful lot. And worry about him. And read books about his country. I don't really even *like* him much, so there's no reason I should spend all my time thinking about him. I just can't help it. I have this urge to find out, and then, whatever's happened to him, begins to happen to me.

'Do you have any special worries, Simon? At school, or at home, or with exams?'

Patti was there in the surgery, listening.

Yes, you could say that having seen one's sister die in resettlement camp, and one's mother shot in a pit, and one's father blown up by his own land-mine, one might have quite a lot of stresses on. And I don't know what's going to happen next. We are alone and lost. And the chief worry of all is that everybody knows that these things happened and they've all decided to forget. Even Ha himself has begun to forget. I just hope *I* don't forget.

But the doctor seemed so detached and clinical that even if I'd been alone with him, I wouldn't have said anything.

'No, I don't think so,' I said. 'Everything's pretty normal, thank you.'

I could see Pattie was relieved. But I still had a headache so

156

they sent me to Aunt Claire's for a rest just like the troops were sent off to Hong Kong or Sydney for rest and recreation when the strain of fighting was too much. They called it R and R.

While I was with Aunt Claire, there were no dreams, no flashing lights, nothing. This time, they gave me Sophie's room. It was filled with her dollies, and picture books. But I hardly noticed. I slept solid for two days, right through. When I finally woke, the headache was completely gone. I felt rested and clear-thinking.

It was early evening, Sophie and Ben's bath-time. They were like fat, pink fish in their bath, slippery with soap and giggling. Little Ben could sit now by himself. He was at one end of the bath, and Sophie at the other was showing him how to play with the plastic bath toys.

'Thith ith the way you do it, Ben,' she said. 'You puth it along threw the wather tho it goth very fasth.'

The baby blew bubbles and grinned. Sophie handed him the plastic boat.

While they played, Claire was perched on the edge of the bath reading the paper.

'Ah, look, here's big cousin Simon. Awake like Rip Van Winkle. How're you feeling after the sleep of a hundred years?'

I said I was better.

'Good, go down then and make yourself comfy. Mike'll be home soon and we'll eat. Now come along, my tots. Better get you washed and bedded. Then I can go and look after your Daddy and hungry Simon.'

Sophie began to wash her baby brother's neck with a flannel. She was vigorous but he seemed to like it.

Claire lifted first one then the other child up out of the water, and wrapped each in a towel and sat them one on each knee.

'What's the story going to be tonight?' she asked.

'No thtory,' said Sophie. 'I'm going to weed the thtory mythelf, and I'm going to weed it to Ben, too.'

'Can she *really* read?' I said. She'd not begun school yet.

'No, of course not. Not the words. But she loves reading the pictures aloud to Ben. She gets into his cot and reads aloud the pictures.'

We had a good evening together. After two days sleeping, I was hungry. Claire was a different sort of cook from my mother. Claire's was all instant, oven-ready, no time-waste food — two enormous pizzas from the deep-freeze, ready-made coleslaw out of plastic tubs, cans of coke. She didn't go in for laying a table either. We ate it off our knees, round the fire with the television on. They didn't ask questions all the time, or go in for earnest discussions. They just wanted to make me happy. I knew I didn't deserve it.

I could probably have stayed in lazy comfort for weeks. Sleep all day amongst Sophie's dolls, feed all evening, watch television. Spoiled and petted by my aunt and uncle, admired distantly by my small cousins. But I couldn't stay. I had to get back. Like the soldiers at R and R centres in Hong Kong, you don't forget what it is you've been sent away from, not when you know you've got to get back to it.

'You can't go yet!' said Claire. 'You're meant to be here for the full rest-cure.'

'I *am* rested,' I said. 'I feel marvellous.'

'But everybody's expecting you to stay at least a week.'

Uncle Mike nodded and passed me a packet of salted cashew nuts.

'You're not afraid of those dreams you told me you used to have?' said Claire.

'No. I just want to go back home now.'

In rushing wildly about, thinking people should be got rid of, I'd mishandled the whole situation. I'd tried to find a solution which was far too complicated, too violent, too destructive. It wasn't that Ha had to be got rid of, nor that I had to be got rid of. Nobody had to be got rid of. It was simpler than that. We both had to stay. And I had to work out a way of living in the same house without being repelled by his presence.

'Won't you stop here at least till tomorrow?'

'I'd rather go tonight, if you don't mind. But thanks for having me.'

'Well, I suppose you know best,' said Claire doubtfully. 'We'll ring your mother. She'll be glad, anyway, to know you prefer her cooking to mine.'

'It's not the cooking, honestly. I think your food's great. It's just, well I can't explain, but I need to see Ha about something.'

Mike drove me home in his Rover. Patti was waiting for me on the doorstep.

'Welcome *home*, darling!' she said. 'How *are* you?' It was as though I'd been away for years. 'We *are* glad to have you back, though I do wish you'd stayed at Claire's just a little longer, and really got over it.'

'Got over *what*? I've got to go to school tomorrow. I've missed enough as it is.'

The moment I was inside, I knew something funny was going on. The house was like a graveyard, dead.

Tony had coffee ready on a tray, two strong black, one milky, just as usual, and we sat quietly and sedately.

'How's Ha?' I said.

'Fine,' said Patti. 'His usual bouncy self.'

I wanted to ask, 'Did he miss me? Did he notice I'd been away?' Instead, I said, 'He in bed already?'

Patti glanced sideways at Tony, then at me.

'He's not here any more,' she said.

'What d'you mean, not here?' I stood up, splashing coffee on the carpet, and I realized what was missing from home. All signs of Ha were gone. His funny misshapen shoes on the hall floor, his mess of Lego bricks scattered in every corner. His photograph from the mantelpiece, even his smell was missing.

'Has he gone back to The Chestnuts?'

'No, he's being fostered with another family, a very good family.'

'How *could* you!' I sat down again.

'We'll be able to see him in the holidays. Maybe even have him back for a weekend now and then.'

'You shouldn't have!' I shouted.

'Simon darling,' Patti began, and then started to cry.

Ha's mother never cried. Not even at the end. Ha's mother was a strong, whole woman, not soft and used to Western comforts.

'Whenever anything gets difficult, that's your escape, isn't it!' I said. 'You just start crying.'

'Simon!' said Tony. 'Don't talk to your mother like that.' But he didn't reach out and try to console her. He was cold and dead too.

'She's not crying because she's sad,' I said. 'She's only crying because she feels guilty. She *knows* it was wrong to send him away.'

Patti sobbed louder than ever. 'It's not true. I just don't know *why* I'm crying.'

'And anyway, we didn't send him away,' said Tony. 'The social worker took him.'

'Typical!' I said. 'And where's she taken him? If you won't

have him here, I'll go and live wherever he is.'

'We don't have his address,' said Tony.

'You mean, you don't even know *where* she took him?'

'Miss Spaark said we can get in touch with the foster mother any time, through her. She said it would be easier for everybody that way. Try for a clean break, she said.'

Neither of them said they'd done it for me. They didn't explain that when there was a choice of sons, they chose me. When Ha was here, they kept telling me how much they loved me. Now he wasn't here, they didn't say anything about love. All their loving had gone out of the front door with Ha. There was none left at home.

'We have to look at the positive things that came out of the experience,' said Tony.

'Like what?' I couldn't think of a single positive thing.

'Well, think of all that we achieved for Ha which would never have happened if he hadn't come to us. He doesn't scream any more. Apparently, the new foster mother said she couldn't believe he'd *ever* had screaming fits, he seemed such a gentle little chap. Isn't it good to think we helped him in that way? And he doesn't *bite*! And he doesn't run berserk. And he doesn't spit any more.'

They were all negative. A list of wonderful things he *didn't* do any more.

'I can think of just *one* positive thing that's come out of it,' I said. It had shown me that we weren't a close, united family after all, and we probably never had been. They were a couple who hadn't much feeling for each other. And I was the difficult son, like a thorn in their flesh. When Ha was here, they could at least feel that they were doing somebody some good. With only me, it was going to be very hard to feel they were doing anybody anything.

'So now, we must remember the benefits we achieved for Ha, and concentrate on being a proper family again.'

'Some family!' I said. We would never be a family again. We were each in our separate corners. Ha had invaded our household like the roots of a weed, burrowing into every crack. And now that he'd been pulled out, there was nothing left but space.

'God, I wish I'd never been born,' I said as I left the room. You can always upset parents if you say that. It's like a kick in the face to them.

160

I didn't sleep well. I don't suppose they did either. I missed Ha. Mostly I missed his rocking. I tried to rock myself, but it wasn't the same thing.

I knew I had to get him back. It wasn't really Ha I wanted. It was his rocking and his dreams.

I was addicted to war, not any war, but *his* war. I could read as many books as I liked about it. But they weren't the same. Only with Ha there could I remember the violence, the fear, the smell of rotting flesh, the leeches, as they really were.

3

In the dinner hour I went to the place where Miss Spaark worked. I didn't know the telephone number. I wished I hadn't thrown away her card.

In the entrance hall of the building, there was a woman behind a glass window. She slid it open.

'Yes?'

'Miss Spaark,' I said.

'You have an appointment?'

'No.'

'I'll ring through and see if she's in. Who shall I say it is? Oh, hello? Yes, main door here. Is Janice in? There's a young man to — No, all right.'

The woman behind the glass panel turned to me. 'No, dear, she doesn't seem to be in her office at the moment, though I'm sure I saw her around earlier. I'd better take your name and say you called, shall I?' Then she seemed to look at me closely, as though memorizing my face, and leaned right forward, practically through her little sliding window.

'Is it urgent, dear? I mean, maybe you'd like to speak to somebody else? In confidence of course, if it's private.'

Maybe she was staring at my hair? I felt it to see if it was standing on end. It seemed all right. But I realized that the rest of me was a bit strange. I'd left my blazer in the classroom. I was hot and sweaty from running all the way from school, and my shirt was half untucked from my trousers. I hurriedly tucked it in. Perhaps she thought I was a child running away from one of Miss Spaark's children's homes.

'Nope,' I said. 'Doesn't matter.'

'I'll put a message for her, to say who called.'

'Just say it was a friend.'

'I have to have a name.'

'It really doesn't matter,' I said. 'It's not important.'

Why did I say that when it *was* very important?

'I say, dear.' The woman called after me through her sliding window, but I was already across the entrance hall. I had to get out of here and think of something else. Move on to Plan B. If only there *was* a Plan B. There hadn't even been a Plan A.

I pushed through the swing doors, and bumped into Miss

Spaark breezing in.

'Goodness!' she shrieked, picking up her handbag and tossing back her hair. '*You*, here!'

I followed her across the hall, up some stairs, along a corridor, to her office. It was grey. Grey lino tiles, grey tin desk, grey walls, grey plastic lamp. So dull. I'd imagined that with her bright yellow hair and her red trousers and scarlet fingernails, she'd work in a rainbow-coloured room.

She flopped down behind her tin desk.

'I've come to see about getting Ha back,' I said.

She laughed. 'Simon, it was only a trial. You always knew that. Sometimes these things work out right first time. Sometimes they don't. You needn't feel your family's *failed* in any way. Nobody's failed. In the short time he was with your family, he benefited enormously. The rich environment, the stimulation, the stability all did him so much good.'

I didn't think we'd failed. And I didn't think it was only a trial. Nor did I think we had benefited him enormously. That was the same line she'd spun to my parents. But I didn't interrupt. I just kept quiet as she told me how happily Ha had gone off in her car when she fetched him, to be driven to the new foster family. He hadn't cried, or been upset at all. He had seemed to understand perfectly what was happening.

'He really was so sensible, and he packed up all his own little toys himself.'

'Yep. I know. In *my* rucksack,' I muttered.

'Probably, it's thanks to his stay with you,' Miss Spaark prattled on, 'that he's been able to stabilize so quickly in his new family.'

Nor did I want to believe that.

'Her four children are all grown-up and she has three smaller foster children with her.'

That meant she must be old. Older than Patti, older than Ha's first mother, perhaps even as old as Ha's grandmother.

I said, 'His other mother was very young, and very pretty.'

'And she's very experienced. We specially chose a professional foster-mother this time.'

'Professional? What d'you mean? She's *paid* to do it?'

'Yes.'

'But you can't *pay* someone to love someone. That's like hiring mercenaries to fight your wars. Paying men to be killers for any old cause, even if they don't believe in it!'

163

'We have a number of professional foster-parents on our books who are specially chosen for their skilled parenting. And, at this stage, we feel that this is just the place for Ha. It's all working out very well for him.'

'Where does she live, this *professional* woman?'

'In the area. We'll be able to ensure he goes on at the same school.'

We. We. We. As though Ha was her property. I hadn't noticed Ha belonging to her when he screamed at night, or needed his nappy changing, or bit Patti's arm so hard it bled.

'What's the address?'

'I'm afraid his exact whereabouts must remain confidential. For his own safety, and yours. For everybody's peace of mind.'

'OK. That's fine by me. You needn't tell me where he is.' I got up and went to the door. 'Just get him back. That's all. He's got to come back and you know it perfectly well.' I left, slamming the door behind me.

I went to her office every day for a week. If she wasn't there, I waited till she came in. And I always said the same thing.

But just being single-minded and insistent wasn't having any effect. I tried a new approach.

'Listen, you told me, right at the beginning, that the feelings of the other children in a family counted as much as the new one. Right? You went on and on about it, remember? And how important I was in the whole scheme. You said, it was no good saving one child's happiness, if you destroyed another child's. Well, you happen to have destroyed my happiness, by taking Ha without asking me. All that talk about how my opinion mattered! But did you bother to *ask* my opinion about whether Ha should go?'

Miss Spaark twiddled a long curl of hair round her finger.

'Well, did you say that or not?' I shouted across her desk. 'That I mattered? That my opinion counted?' It was a louder shout than I meant it to be.

'Simon, this was always a very difficult case. Ha is a most unusual child with unexpected problems all along the line. You know that as well as I do.'

'I'm not talking about what anybody thinks they know. I'm talking about what you said. All that stuff, about how, as the new brother, *I* was the real expert. About how I'd get to know what was best for Ha, probably better than anybody else. Have you forgotten? Or d'you say that to all adoptive families? Was it just lies to win me round?'

She reached across her desk for a pad and began to scribble things. Notes about me and my unpredictable behaviour.

'He may be just another difficult case to you. To me, he is my brother!' I quite surprised myself by saying it. It slipped out before I had time to stop it.

'Miss Spaark, would you please look at me when I'm trying to speak to you? I may be merely a small aspect of this difficult case, but please treat me as a human while I'm in the room. And please answer the question which I'm asking for the third time. Were you lying when you said my opinions about Ha mattered, and that they would be taken into account?'

'Of course you matter, Simon. But you're obviously a highly emotional child who has already shown signs of considerable disturbance.' She reached out for the grey telephone. But I got there first, flinging myself across her desk, grabbing the phone and throwing it on to the floor where it landed with a hollow clatter and a single feeble ping.

She looked at me almost frightened. Social worker trapped alone in grey office with disturbed sub-adolescent boy. She seemed unsure what I was going to do next. I was unsure myself.

'It's all right, Miss Spaark. I won't do anything dangerous, provided you give me some of your professional attention. Because I am a severely disturbed child. If you don't attend to my problems, I may end up in Care as well. That's not going to look very good in your records, is it? Adoption worker assesses home, and gives it her approval. Into the family, she places dum-dum child. Then she changes her mind and removes dum-dum child. Natural child goes mad and is also put in Care. Two kids in Care instead of one. However, if I *don't* go mad, and it all works out, you'll have a success. Two children happy. Council's money saved. Promotion.' I wasn't too sure about the last bit. Perhaps she didn't need promotion? Perhaps she was already at the top.

She smiled slyly. 'It's very thoughtful of you, Simon, to have worked it all out. But these things take time. It's a very necessary safeguard, to prevent children yo-yoing about. There's a lot of paperwork involved, and it can't be done quickly.'

Oh no? It hadn't taken her much time to get him removed and into somewhere else. About one day as far as I could gather.

'He just must come back,' I said.

She got up from behind the protection of her grey metal desk, bent down and picked up her telephone.

'May I?' she asked, dialling a number. 'Call my secretary?' Now she was flattering me.

'Hello, Jean. Any calls for me in the next hour, say I'm in conference. I'll call back later.'

Being in conference seemed a grand way of saying having a chat.

'We'll go out,' she said. 'It's sometimes easier to talk in the open.'

She was right. Without the four grey walls of her office pressing in, I felt safer. She couldn't make notes about me while I was talking. Even so, I sensed her making notes in her head. It must be terrible to be a real child in Care, knowing your social worker is noting down every move you make.

She was awful, but not quite as awful as she'd seemed at the beginning. Once she'd decided to listen, she was quite good at it. I talked about Ha's country. About the climate, the way the village people lived, the fairy stories they tell their children, the Festivals they celebrate, the kind of food they eat.

'I was thinking of making him a little scrap-book about his country. Specially about the food because he likes food a lot. You know, about roast cassava roots, and nuam nuoc sauce. They have that with everything. And the avocadoes.'

'I thought they just ate rice?'

'During the war they had to because they often weren't able to stay in their villages and see to the crops. But the rice they usually got given was very old and bad. Bulgar wheat mostly, and it'd been stored too long. That's why so many got ill. It hadn't any Vitamin C left in it. Fresh rice has, just like any other fresh crop.'

'Well I never! You're a bright lad.'

'Well, my mother *is* a nutritionist,' I said. 'So I'm probably a bit more interested in food than most boys.'

'That scrap-book's a good idea. As a matter of fact, we usually make a book of memories like that when our children are placed for adoption. Snaps of their natural parents, old birthday cards, and so on. It seems to help them settle. But somehow, in Ha's case, it rather got left out. Anyway, I'm not sure he'd understand too well.'

Since she liked the idea of the scrap-book, I elaborated on how I'd begun to collect advertisements from the Sunday colour supplements of exotic eastern scenes, tropical fish markets, and beautiful, slant-eyed air hostesses on Malaysian Air Lines.

'So he'll be able to identify with his own race,' I explained. 'I know Malays aren't *really* the same as his people, but it's a start.'

What rubbish I was talking. I hadn't begun to make any sort of scrap-book, let alone collect pictures. Any scraps I'd got were all inside my head, and they weren't tourist trip pictures either. But I didn't tell her any of the real things I knew about Ha's country, about being in the pit, about the weight of bodies in the steamy heat, about the fear of being alone.

Where the riverside walk crosses over the main street, there's a new hamburger joint just opened up.

'Don't suppose you had any dinner yet?' she said.

I hadn't. She bought me a paper cone of chips. I think it made her feel good to buy me chips and watch me eating them. To do something so obviously beneficial for me was satisfying for her. Feed a hungry child and you feel instantly better, as though merely by giving him food you have eased all his problems.

We sat on the grass sloping down to the river. Office workers were lounging in the sun and ducks were waddling along the bank looking for sandwich crusts.

'You see,' I said, 'there were quite a lot of reasons why it was difficult at first, when Ha came.' I told her about being an only child, and then suddenly, not being an only child. 'Though I *would* have had a sister, if Patti's baby had survived.'

She didn't say anything, but seemed startled. She'd never heard about the stillborn sister.

I finished the chips.

'Those are the excuses about why it was hard at first. I think we're through that now, and if he did come back, I feel we could now give him the love he really deserves.' I liked that phrase. It sounded like the kind of thing she might say. The love he really deserves.

I felt I'd succeeded in making a good overall impression of being a fundamentally calm and sensible person which would counteract my earlier outburst. Of course I didn't tell her the real reasons why I needed Ha back. It was nothing to do with love, or roast cassava roots, or Patti's dead baby. But I suspected that if I'd told her that I needed Ha because I missed the sound of gunfire in the night, and the whirling of chopper blades, I dare say she'd have had him fostered as far as she could, to Aberdeen or Penzance.

'It's been very useful talking with you, Simon,' she said. 'And I'll think over what you've said. Now you should be getting back to school, I imagine?'

We both got to our feet and walked back towards town. 'And as a matter of fact, Simon, what you're suggesting might well be the answer.' I began to understand why she had been so attentive to me. It was nothing to do with me making a good impression. 'You see, Simon, as a matter of fact I do still have quite a problem on my hands with Ha's case. I'd better be frank with you.'

Great. Marvellous. Thank you, social worker. Frankness at last.

'This is strictly confidential, you understand? It's simply not working out with the new foster-family. Mrs Blishen, I mean the foster-mother, rang me yesterday. She said he can't stay there after all.'

'Why not?' I tried to sound calm.

'She feels, well she feels it's not the right place for him. He's so strange. He upsets the other foster-children. But since you're a bit strange too —' Miss Spaark laughed. 'Well maybe we should give it another try.'

Didn't it occur to her even now that it was the presence of Ha which made children near him get a bit strange?

So Ha would be returned to us. His stay with Mrs Blishen would be referred to, not as a failed fostering, but as a useful period of temporary respite. And nobody lost face, least of all Miss Spaark.

4

I came back from school and Ha was back. I almost hugged him, except that he was too engrossed in television to be bothered with me. Besides, I was too busy finding my way round my own house. It all looked different. Patti and Tony had gone and reorganized every room.

'What on *earth* have you moved all the furniture round for?' I said.

They must have spent hours shifting beds, books, tables, chairs. Up and down the stairs. The dining-room was going to become their bedroom. Their bedroom was going to be Ha's bedroom, rubber undersheet, old cereal cartons, furry wabbits and all. The single bunk-bed looked so small where there used to be a wide double bed, while downstairs, the double bed completely swamped the dining-room. It didn't look in the least bit like a bedroom.

I still had my own room, how it used to be in the old days. Before Ha. Before I knew anything.

I told them, 'You've got to put Ha's bed back in my room. And all his things. We must have the rooms as they were.'

'But darling, Ha gives you bad dreams! He makes so much noise in the night. It's much better this way.'

'I *want* to sleep with Ha,' I said. 'We must get the beds back before tonight. I'll help.'

So we put it all back again how it should be with Ha sleeping in the bunk-bed below me.

And then, I went to bed early and nothing happened. If I dreamed of anything at all, it was about sunny days. Nothing useful. And Ha slept all through the night, stretched out on his back like a baby, luxuriantly, his arms spread above his head, small, open brown palms, unclenched. His legs out, relaxed, his mouth slightly open. No rocking.

The second night, the same. Less than two weeks away with the professional foster-person, and he'd stopped rocking.

'He's dry!' said Patti. 'Isn't it amazing? That respite with the temporary foster-mother must have been so good for him! Just what he needed.'

She'd got him dry. She'd stopped him dribbling. She'd stopped him humming. Stopped him wanting to wear his anorak at breakfast. She'd stopped him rocking. She'd done marvels.

'But she didn't want to keep him, did she?' I said. 'She was just a paid professional who did her job, like a soldier is paid to kill.'

I watched Ha sleeping, his legs stretched out to their full extent because he wasn't sleeping in a tent, or a forest, or a foxhole, or in a cardboard box beside the road, but in a bed.

He half woke and smiled.

'Shimoo,' he said. 'Nice boy.' And turned over to sleep again.

'Why aren't you rocking any more? Come on!' I roared at him. 'Rock, can't you!' He used to react to shouts. Not any more. I took him by the shoulders and shook him.

I grabbed hold of the metal bedframe and shook it hard to try and start him rocking. No rocking, but at least he was awake, sitting up, smiling his trusting angel smile at me and clutching his blue wabbit. I stopped shaking the bed and sat down beside him.

'Ha, do you like it here, living with Patti and Tony as your mum and dad?'

'Not talk,' said Ha, and grinned his gap-toothed grin. But it wouldn't be gap-toothed for long. The beginning of a new, crooked tooth was showing. All that wonderful calcium Patti gave him to eat in high-protein breakfasts.

'We have to talk. It's important. You've got to remember things. What happened to you? Why did you stop being able to do anything? Who were those people who took you out of your cardboard box? Where did they take you? Did you get to another camp, or to prison, or where?'

'Not listen.'

'All right. You needn't listen. But *I'm* still going to talk. I'm going to tell a story even if you don't listen to it. About a boy in a village who lost everything when the soldiers came, even his family. And there was a war going on all round him with rockets and noise.'

'No!' he said. 'No. No. No. Not listening.'

'And something happened to him. Look at yourself, Ha. You can't even dress yourself. You can't walk properly. But once you could understand plenty of things. You knew how to work all day in the fields. You even helped dismantle an M-113. You knew perfectly well how to take care of yourself alone in the forest.'

Suddenly, he began to cry, not mad, senseless screaming like he used to, but the ordinary, sad crying with tears.

I put my arms round him, and hugged him better. 'You see, Ha,

I know things about you, the horrible things as well as the other. But I don't know it all. I want to know everything.'

'Don't know thing.'

'Yes, you do. I know you do, and you've got to let me know too. I got you back to live here. And now we've got to work out a good way of living together. We're like the men from the North, and the men from the South. We have to share the same place. But you see, Ha, it's more difficult for me because I was here first. So I'm having to do *all* the sharing. Sharing my home, my parents, my Lego, my toys, my room. You haven't got that sort of thing to share. So you've got to share something else. D'you see? You've got to share your war with me. And since you're too stupid to tell me about it in language, you'll have to share it the other way. Now shove up, and make room for me beside you.'

I got into his bed and the rubber sheet crackled beneath us. We lay down and I held him and his wabbit in my arms and I rocked him backwards and forwards till the whole bunk-bed with both of us on it was swaying like a hammock. Then we got right back there to the stifling humid heat in the middle of his war.

Soon, the women with faces like moons in the sky, who were collecting the fools off the street, and the cretins, and the frightened, found a baby. It wasn't moving but they took it along all the same.

'The poor little kid. It's terrible, just left there in the dirt.'

The pick-up van stopped in a dusty courtyard in front of a large building. We got out as we were told, except the dead baby which fell out. The two women didn't know what to do with it. One picked it up and nursed it.

'If only we'd got there sooner. We might have saved it.'

'We'll have to bury it.'

'We can't do that. What about their formalities? Certificates or registering? If we go against their regulations, they might take away our permits.'

My legs were so tired. I sat down on the ground. The place they'd brought us to was already full. Toddlers shuffled along the open verandas. Children sat in the courtyard. Babies lay.

But even though they had plenty of other babies, the two women seemed more concerned about the dead one. The woman who was holding it ran across the courtyard and out through the gates.

'Don't go out, Pam!' the other shouted at her. 'Please don't. Wait till after curfew. You'll only get arrested.'

But she went and I saw her speak to a uniformed man in the street. She came slowly back, crying.

'What did he say?' said the other woman.

'I didn't understand, something about being a policeman, not an undertaker.'

They seemed to care a lot for the baby. They buried it in a corner of the courtyard with a bunch of pink flowers on the mound. But when it was time for the Festival of Tombs, who would visit the grave and tidy it, burn the paper piastres over it, offer the prayers? The child had no descendants to care for her grave, so her soul would certainly wander for ever.

Were you afraid, Ha that you too might die and be buried? Didn't you want to get up and run away?

No, I was too tired to be afraid.

I stayed sitting by the wall, watching. A cauldron of rice was cooked and the children ran to it, and lined up, each with a tin bowl. I watched them, but I didn't join in. My legs didn't want to move. They didn't want to carry me any further. I looked at them stretched out in front of me on the dusty ground. They'd carried me far enough. I wasn't surprised when I found they didn't work any more.

When the women saw that I couldn't walk they propped me on a bench and brought a bowl of rice and put it in my lap. But the other children discovered they could take my rice from me. They could push me and topple me from my perch. So one of the women carried me over her shoulder out of their reach, up a flight of dark stone steps to a room on the first floor.

She placed me in a cot with wooden sides. It was built for a baby and my legs buckled up. But it didn't matter because I didn't need them any more.

I had soiled myself, so she wiped me with a wet cloth and wrapped another cloth loosely round me held in place with a metal pin she took from the baby in the next cot.

She didn't have a name. She had a face which could have been any woman's face. I wasn't going to remember her name or her face. She was just a woman who was going to look after me.

Sometimes, she might be a different woman, but it didn't matter because this place is now my home. I will stay here for weeks, or years, or for the rest of my life and I don't need ever to walk, or crawl, or talk again. They've given me food and a place to lie down, just as hens and goats and buffaloes are given food and a place to lie down.

Ha! You must wake up. You must sit up and look around you. You've come to a home for orphans. There's not going to be enough food here for you all. When you get ill, there's not going to be enough medicine, not enough help. Soon, your body will be covered with rashes, your hair caked with dirt. You'll be lying in your own wetness till your skin is raw. When the flies settle, you'll be too listless even to push them away. You must sit up, Ha, before it's too late. You must wake up and leave.

I still remember the story my grandmother told me, of Tu Thuc who made the biggest mistake of his life. He found the Land of Bliss, the land of eternal youth, where he never grew old, never needed to labour, where food was always supplied to him. But the foolish young man grew restless. He asked to leave the Land of Bliss, to revisit his old village and find his origins. But once he'd left the Land of Bliss, he could never find his way back to it again.

I shan't do that. I will stay forever in the world of eternal youth.

Ha, do you see black flies hovering over you? Do you see cockroaches lurking in the cracks of the crumbling plaster walls? Do you see vermin on the tiled floors? Do you smell the sour drains blocked with filth? Do you smell the lingering odour of unwashed human children? Do you hear the strange, unnatural quiet of hopeless children who never cry?

No, I see nothing to fear, hear nothing to disturb me, smell nothing to disgust me. I have reached the Land of Bliss where all is perfection. I draw my world in round me because when I turn my head and peer through the bars of this cot, I see that the other occupants are ugly. Their stomachs rounded and swollen. Their legs like twigs. Their ribs bulging like birdcages. Their skin stretched tightly over their bones. I am glad I am not like that.

173

But Ha, listen to me, you *were* like that!

I am a baby. I can't hear what you're saying.

I said, you looked just the same as the rest. All of you, in that room, you were the children of the streets. You too have become part of the dust of life.
I like it. To be part of the dust of life is to be safe.

5

When they sluiced the floors with a hose, they used to take the babies and defectives downstairs to the courtyard for fresh air. We sat, propped by the wall, twiddling our toes in the puddles, and watching the clever children splashing in the drains which overflowed in the rains.

But soon there were too many of us and it took too long to carry us down the stairs and up again. Besides, the women were always changing. Each had her own method of doing things.

The new helpers put us out on to the veranda alongside our room. After they had hosed the floor of the room, they hosed us where we sat, and the water splashed over the edge of the veranda on to the older children playing in the yard below.

We couldn't see them, but we heard their voices. The veranda was cool. The floor was smooth, patterned in black and white tiles. I looked at the tidy patterns, one square tile followed another in an orderly sequence.

But a boy with a weak spine toppled slowly forwards and fell across the black and white tiles where I had been staring. His head banged on the stone. His head was in the way of my looking. So I leaned forward and touched him. My fingers fastened round his thick, matted hair.

The feel was good. I held tighter and pulled. That was good. He moaned. The woman came. She sat him upright and she slapped me round the head. That was good to. I liked her hand touching my head. I liked the feeling of being touched and slapped, and the ringing in my ears. I called out so that she'd hit me again.

'Come on now. Up you get.' I struggled because I wanted to stay on the veranda today. I cried, and tried to tell her that I wanted to stay with the black and white pattern. But she didn't understand me. I had let everything go and now I'd even let my speaking fade. The more I struggled in her arms, the more firmly they grasped me. So I bit her, and another nameless woman appeared to carry me back into the stifling room.

Some women were like us, with dark hair and skin. Some were round-eyes, with pale hair, pale faces.

Two new women came and washed us, not with a hose, but one at a time, in a sink. And they took a sharp blade from a razor, heated it up in a bright flame, cut open the boils on our hands, and cleaned the cavity.

One of these women didn't like our home. She stared at us, then picked up a child from a cot and cuddled it to comfort herself.

'Put it down, Jane. There's no time for that. If you've come here to work, you'd better get on with it. We've thirty-two in here needing feeds. And that's before we start on the well ones next door, then the ones downstairs.'

'But it's so dreadful! How can you bear it? They're all so dirty, and no sooner have you cleaned up one lot, than the next lot needs it. And they don't have enough food.'

'They're humans, Jane. They're people, just like you and me. They're not dogs, or things. We're here to help, not to wonder why.'

'But if they're going to die anyway, what's the point?'

'At least we'll know they've died with a little dignity.'

'There's no dignity in this place.'

'You'll get used to it. Listen, dear, you're new out here. You'll soon learn that if you waste time picking each one up, another will pass away while your back's turned. So it's better to grit your teeth and do what you can.'

Some days I remembered things and I wanted to tell somebody.

I'm listening, Ha. You can tell me.

Long ago, I remembered the woman in the loose white shirt, with the thick, dark hair, who used to smile at me as she cooked vegetables over the fire beside our house. The man who loved the woman who loved me, lived in an earth tunnel in the forest. The baby girl I used to hold in my lap crowed and gurgled.

But they were fading, just as the land had faded, and the ancestors' tombs had disappeared into the earth. There was nobody left to tell and there was nothing left to tell about.

Yes, Ha, there is. I want to know about it. I care. Tell me.

The girl-child in the cot beside me was Phuong. Only a few of the children in the room had names.

One morning, Phuong ceased to move. When the woman came into the room with the feeding bottles of milk, she peered into the cot, touched the bundle and when she lifted it up it didn't even flutter. She removed the feeding bottle and gave it to me instead, and she took Phuong away.

Once, I had seen another kind of dying which was filled with sudden violent movement and fear frozen to a child's face. Phuong had no fear.

They called the next one in that cot Phuong too. Perhaps it was the name of the cot which was Phuong, not the child? In that case, I was not Ha, but the cot in which I lay was Ha. My world, which enclosed me with wooden bars from behind my head, down to my feet, was Ha, and while I lay safe in this world, I was Ha. But if I left this world, I would cease to be Ha. If I ceased to be Ha, I was nothing.

Once, long ago, I was happy living in a village. But they moved us from there to a place where we lived in tents. After the tents, I wandered through the rubber trees with the woman with the smiling face. And after her, I was alone.

Now we live here, each in our small cage, in a room for sickly infants and defectives.

You're not a defective, Ha! You're a casualty of war.

Day by day, as I lie safe behind my bars, I have time to remember a place where we lived in tents.

There were always a lot of pigs, but nowhere to keep them. The people who'd brought their pigs with them had to tie them to the tent poles to stop them wandering. It was hot in camp. By midday, the pigs wanted nothing but shade. So they lay down in the nearest tent, on top of the people inside, just to be out of the sun.

The family next to us had a large, fully grown pig, grey, muddy, and bristly. It always came to our tent to lie down, and the old woman with red-stained teeth I lived with, heaved at it, and poked it with a stick to try and move it. But she wasn't strong enough. The first time that the pig escaped into our tent, it rootled in our cooking pot and ate half our rice. Everybody was angry, so the owner of the pig brought round a present of one of her sleeping mats. It didn't make up for the loss of our supper but it showed that she wanted to try to keep the peace.

After that, they tied their pig to a stronger piece of rope. But the pig was stronger still. In the middle of the night, it pulled the tent down on top of them and even my mother couldn't help laughing. We went to help them put up their tent again.

'I can't think why they don't just set that poor wretched creature free outside in the bush,' my mother said, 'and be done with all this bother!'

She didn't mean it seriously. Nobody was going to set their livestock free when we'd be going home soon. Perhaps my mother was jealous that we had no pig, only a hen, and a goat whose milk had dried up. The goat was always hungry. There wasn't enough green stuff for it and it began to chew holes in our tent. Then it was the turn of the people beside us to laugh. But when the goat nibbled the tops of the sprouting beans it wasn't funny any more. So I swung my head from side to side, this way and that across the cot, creating a comforting, rocking movement which seemed to soothe me. And I stopped remembering the time when I used to live in a tent.

'They keep them like animals here! How can they keep them like this!'

'It's the stench that got me. The first time I came in here, I was actually sick, just from the smell, but you get used to it.'

As the woman lifted me up over the sink to wash my back, I saw myself in a piece of broken mirror propped up above the taps. I saw a face like a monkey with dark eyes sunk in like black stones. Above the head, there was hardly any hair, only bald patches and small, sparse tufts.

I stared at myself and I wanted to tell her something. I couldn't remember what it was. I think I wanted to tell her that I hadn't always looked like this, hadn't always lived here. I had a place where I belonged, and people I belonged with, but when I tried to think of it, I couldn't remember who I was, or where I was.

I reached up to the black wisps of fluff on top of my head, grabbed hold and pulled. The hair came away quite easily.

You're beginning to starve, Ha. You're a casualty of war. And the war isn't just out in the far-away forests. It's moving closer. It's coming into the city.

At night, you hear tumbling bombs, detonating shells. You hear crackling gun-fire. You hear screaming planes skim out over your city, and you see their black shapes flash by your window, with red lights twinkling on the underside.

You can feel the earth rumbling.

At night, our room was in darkness and we were left alone. Some children slept through, only jolting and twitching in their sleep when a heavy noise shook the room. The sounds were too close. Sometimes I could smell the smell of burning. Sometimes I could hear voices crying, and shouts and running feet in the street. But nobody came to us and told us what it meant.

Then, our room was lit by a spray of coloured light. I saw the rows of cots and the other children. A window shattered and pieces of shining glass flew through the air and scattered across the room. Some fell on the concrete floor. Some fell in Phuong's bed and she began to whimper. She woke the others and soon the room was filled with plaintive moaning. Nobody came.

But we weren't alone. Something was in our room, slithering along the floor. I saw the dark shape sliding towards my cot. It stopped and lay directly beneath me. And I heard it breathing. When it grew light, I saw it was an injured man.

Towards morning, the gunfire ceases. The cock crows. The curfew ends and you hear, outside, the clatter and chatter as traders set up market stalls on the pavement. Even in wartime.

At last the women came with the feeding-bottles. They propped a bottle into the first ten cots while they washed the children from the next ten cots. The bottles were refilled, and put into the cots of the next. Rush, rush. They always hurried. I reached out my hands and grabbed my bottle quickly. If you were slow, they had to take the bottle from you before it was empty.

The man's hand stretched up to my cot, reaching through the bars, groping across the mattress, searching. His face came up behind the bars, following his hand, and he looked at me. He seemed to see right through me.

I growled and bared my teeth. I rolled over and bit my teeth into the hand and tasted blood. It wasn't blood I had drawn, but blood already there. I held my bottle firmly and rocked myself vigorously from side to side. I would shake him off. Milk spilled down the sides of my neck. I could not shake him off. His searching hand was strong. His long, brown fingers locked in a tight hold round my feeding-bottle and took it away. The soldier raised the teat to his own mouth.

When he had finished, he tried to feel for my hand. He stroked my bare leg gently with his fingers. But I knew he mustn't touch me.

The women heard me screaming. One came and slapped me, but then she found the man on the floor.

'How on earth did *he* get in?'

'I think it's Co Anh's husband.'

'Go and find her. Someone go and find her.'

'Co Anh! Co Anh! Come up here quickly.'

Co Anh flung herself on the man and cried and repeated his name again and again. They carried him away and they forgot to wash me that day.

Later, they saw Phuong with glass embedded in her leg.

'They must get so bored! Just lolling around in these cots all day. Not able to learn anything, or see what's going on in the world.'

They never had time to talk to us, but I often listened to them talking about us.

'I shouldn't worry. I don't think they're bored. They don't think much. Just as well. If they thought about what's going on in the world, it might make them keel over a bit faster.'

'You're very disillusioned. Don't you feel that you're here doing God's work? You see, I had a vision one night when I was still a student nurse, and so I *know* I was sent here by God to do His work.'

'Good on you.'

'But don't you feel that way?'

'I dare say I did once. But when you've been doing this work for thirteen months, fourteen hours a day, and conditions never get any better, you stop trying to apply meaning. You begin to think that maybe God's got some other quite different meaning that we're not meant to know. Or maybe He's a practical joker, and this is His big anti-creation joke? Who knows?'

'You're very callous.'

'Did you see that baby brought in last week? Perfectly healthy. Now look at her. One week in here and she's dying of dysentery. I don't think I'm in any position to try and put a meaning to that.'

'These local girls, they're hopeless! Won't do anything properly. I said to wash down the children every morning. They never do.'

'It's not their fault. They just haven't been trained.'

'They haven't a clue. About hygiene, not even the basics. They'll change a diaper, then fill the feeders, without even rinsing their hands in between. As for wiping the children's noses. They seem to think it's a waste of time. You'd think they'd at least do what we've shown them!'

'Would you try? If this was your country, if you belonged here and you'd seen it all blown to bits, all your family killed? That's what happened to Binh, the woman who's always smiling, with the long plait. Her whole family wiped out while she was down at the market. When she came back, all gone. It's amazing she carries on. If that sort of thing happened back home, you'd probably be put inside for a while, under psychiatric care, wouldn't you? I know I couldn't cope like she does. I'd just lie down, and stop.'

6

Then two Americans came to visit you. They liked talking to the women helpers who spoke their language. Sometimes they brought presents of dried milk, or chocolate powder, or vitamin drops which the helpers were always pleased to receive. One of the soldiers was black, the other white. They both wore uniform but they didn't carry guns. On their day off, they called in to the orphanage on their way from Hotel Suzy. It made them feel good and clean after they'd been downtown with local girls, to come and look at you in your filthy cots, and to talk to the European nurses.

You used to listen to them talking. The first time they came, they were surprised by your room.

'You look at some of these kids here, and you wonder. What in heck are we doing here? We've no right to be in here. We've orphaned these kids, and half starved them.'

'You know this war is hotting up? It's my guess the US is gonna pull out of here. They're not gonna carry on through. President LBJ got it all wrong.'

'What's gonna happen to all your kids then?'

'We'll be staying on just so long as we can be useful. If the city fell, some of them might be reclaimed by their relatives. We had a woman in the other week, she'd been looking for her child for two months. When their home went, the boy was picked up by IVS workers. That woman went round every orphanage in the city. Then she found him here. It was like a miracle.'

One of the soldiers, the black one, took a special fancy to you.

'I'd like to do something for some of these kids,' he said. 'That little kid there. If I could take that boy back home with me, I would. My wife would understand. She used to be a nursery teacher. I got a boy back home about that age.'

He liked to call you Harvey, because his own boy at home in the States was called Harvey. He used to crouch down by your cot and talk to you through the bars. He was usually drunk when he arrived.

'You know, Harvey, killing's wrong. Even I know that. But this is war. I've wasted people. And so's millions of others like me out there. Between your people and my people. I did what I was told. I was in Korea in two operations. I killed out there. Your lot aren't the first. It just happens that way. But you think I don't have remorse? You know, kid, after I've gone back home, some nights, I'll wake and not sleep and I'll be thinking of you, and wondering what's become of you. Then I'll feel real bad, because you're my special friend.'

He put his hand through the bars of the cot and stroked the back of your hand. He took a small flask from his breast pocket and had another drink.

'The way some people tell it, when you see your buddy blasted, you're raw for revenge. But this war isn't about revenge, not for me it isn't. I'm sorry you're all messed up. And I know what you must be thinking. I guess you could be thinking how it's not right, this war. But, Harvey, them VC do some pretty bad things too. You wouldn't know about any of it, lying there in your crib. But they done wicked things to their own people too, chopping them up and executing them with no fair trial. Some say how communism is like cancer, real evil, sliding along as cunning as a snake. I don't hold with communism myself, but I don't figure it's all that communism as makes them do them bad things, any more than how being God-fearing American makes us want to do killing. I just wish I could understand it. You're a funny kid. You never say anything. But you always look at me as though you know what I'm saying.'

You can't say anything, Ha, can you? You know nothing. You are nothing. You are a dot. You are a digit in the statistics. You are one of a thousand homeless children, one of a hundred thousand, one of eight hundred thousand. You are just a casualty of war.

The soldier got drunker and drunker and began to cry, letting his huge tears from his huge eyes, drop down the sides of your cot. Nothing he said made sense, and in the end you fell asleep. When you woke, he'd gone. He didn't come again, but some time later, one of the women came to you with a red plastic ball from the market. You'd never had a toy like that.

'Look, Harvey. A present. From your friend. Remember your nice friend, the great big soldier?'

'Is he here now? He bring any penicillin? He said he'd try.'

'No. He stepped on a mine. Been invalided home. He got his lieutenant to send this round. See, Harvey, isn't it nice?'

She put the ball in your hands, and you played with it until another child walked up to your room from downstairs and took it away from you.

When my red ball had gone I played with my hands. I had fingers on each hand. When I held them to the light they moved. I had nostrils. I put my finger from one hand into one nostril. I put a finger from the other hand into a nostril. Two hands, two nostrils, and I blew down my nostrils and crowed. I wasn't dead like Phuong in the next bed. I was alive.

I found ear holes in the side of my head and I put my fingers in my ear holes and I blew and crowed and heard noises of rushing wind. I had an umbilical hole in the centre of me. I had two arms. I had a whole body with parts, and with holes to play with. I had my own cage with slatted wooden sides like a hen-coop. It had a friendly smell like a hen-coop. I had urine which passed warmly over me, faeces which slid gently and pleasantly from me.

I had the biggest hole of all in my face, a mouth which opened, into which I put my fingers and sucked them, and as I sucked I rocked my head from side to side.

In the night there was screaming in the sky, and whimpering of babies, and whining of mosquitoes, but I had nostrils to play with, and fingers to suck.

'Maybe he's deaf? That's maybe why he doesn't speak?'

'I don't think he's deaf. He cries in the raids. He's not blind either. He watches me.'

'We could run some tests.'

'Like what tests? Shout in his ear and see if he jumps? Don't be naive. What difference does it make if you prove he's deaf? He can't walk. He can't feed himself. He can barely sit up. There's not much chance for any of them, whatever you manage to prove.'

'But what happens when we leave? Who'll look after them then?'

'Same as before I suppose. Fed twice a day, washed once a day. The local women will just have to get on.'

'We must pray about it. The Lord has an answer.'

'Funny sorts of answers your Lord's given so far. Perhaps you're not praying the right prayer?'

'How many in your room?'

'Twenty-seven. One's got worms. Seventeen skin infections. But we've no talc left. The women keep pinching it and selling it in the market.'

'We can't take in any more. We *must* say no.'

'We can't turn them away.'

'We must tell them to take them to Caritas. We're going to be inspected. We mustn't have them on mats all over the floor.'

'Who's coming?'

'A Government official, and a Red Cross rep.'

'Why? They've never shown interest before. Not when we asked for quinine or tetracyclene, or milk powder.'

'I don't suppose they had the international press round then, did they?'

'Have you heard, we've got to start classifying them.'

'How d'you mean?'

'New regulation. To try and standardize the institutions, a bit of a clamp down on the unofficial ones. Make them better run. The kid's all have to have dossiers, papers, ID cards like everybody else.'

'But half of them haven't even got real *names*, let alone papers. The Ministry of the Interior will never issue cards for kids we know nothing about.'

'We'll just have to sort them out and do what we can.'

'How are we supposed to have time for that sort of thing when it takes all day just to get them fed? We can't start bookwork as well!'

'Come down to the office when you've finished. We'll see what we can do. I've got two beers down there, hidden in the filing cupboard.'

'I see your good Lord's begun answering prayers even before you've had time to pray them.'

They began searching for special children. They peered into cots, they picked out babies. Nobody picked you up. You were too old, you were a boy.

They wanted small, pretty, female children, with a full set of working limbs. Sometimes, they took less pretty boy-children, but only those who had dark skins, the colour of ripe figs, and curly hair and thick, full lips.

Sometimes, money passed hands. How much? A hundred piastres? Or two hundred? Or as much as a water-buffalo? What is a child worth?

They're getting ready for the end, Ha. Tidying up, collecting the orphans with black blood. When they pull out, they don't want to leave behind signs of the occupation.

Sorry, Ha. They don't want you. You're not a half-cast black.

'Why are we only going to take the normal, healthy ones? It doesn't seem fair. Really, we ought to be picking out the weakest ones and leave the rest.'

'We have to select the ones who'll stand the best chance of surviving the journey. We can't have failures. We're aiming for successful adoptions.'

'But it's the weak ones that need rescuing! They're the ones who'll suffer when the end comes.'

'This is not intended as a *rescue* operation. Anyway, we've got to accept the decision of the committee. They clearly ruled out all doubtful mental and physical cases. They said it wouldn't be fair to the child, nor to future adopters. They want only children who stand a hundred per cent chance of responding to a happy family life in the UK.'

'I thought all the would-be adopters were supposed to be Christians? I thought they wanted to help. Not just have a perfect child, carefully screened, free from syphilis, built up with added vitamins.'

'That one, the one they call Ha.'

'I can't remember all their names. They're not real names anyway. Most of them just got given any name anybody could think of when they came in.'

'Well, the large boy, third cot from the middle window.'

'What about him?'

'I just wondered why he's been put in this room? He's too big for the cot. He doesn't seem sick. Why isn't he with the others downstairs?'

'Only God knows why *any* of them are here.'

'What's the doctor think about him?'

'We don't have a doctor. All doctors are kept busy in the military.'

'The health visitor then?'

'There's seven health visitors for the entire city.'

New people came. Something was happening. I watched them walking from cot to cot, up and down the rows. One had a camera on a strap round his neck. I looked through the bars and watched him photographing babies. I had seen a man with a camera before. I remembered it from the past. With memory comes knowledge. The beginning of the loss of something. But I didn't know what it was that had been lost to me.

I watched the group proceeding.

'And this one?'

'We don't know. Anything between nine and thirteen. As you see, he has no teeth.'

'Polio? But he has the use of his arms. The muscle tone seems fair.'

A man lifted one of my legs, then let it drop. He took hold of both my hands to make me sit.

'One of the trained nurses, the Australian, she thought he was probably autistic. She'd worked with autistic children in Melbourne.'

'He responds to very little. Except food. And he smiles. Which seems to rule out autism.'

The man looked at me, held my head in his hand, felt along my arms down to my fingertips. The sensation was good, like water trickling down a stream. But what was a stream?

'One of the girls who was here when I first came, she told me that he used to walk. She said she definitely recalled seeing him walk in here, across the yard. But I don't know how long ago that was.'

'What does it say in the records? About his condition on entering the orphanage?'

'They didn't keep records in those days.'

The man moved my legs again, and my arms. I liked the feeling.

'Where's the woman who said she saw this child walk?'

'That was some time ago. She left three or four years back.'

'Pity. If we could say his deterioration was entirely due to the trauma, and might be reversible, and not due to infection or disease, we might get him on the plane.'

I heard them. I watched them. I knew we were being sorted out, one group from another.

One of the women kept coming to me and waking me in the middle of the day. She bullied me. She wanted me to do things which I couldn't do. She put a rolled blanket behind me so that I had to keep sitting up. She smiled at me and made me smile back. Sometimes, she spoke to me.

'You're a great big lad for this little cot, aren't you now? Come along, laddy, see if you can stand up. Just for a while. Then your legs will have more space.'

But if I was tired, and I was often tired, I fell over sideways.

'Don't whimper like that. Come on. Look bright and alert. I know you can if you try. It'll be no good if you don't try.'

She frightened me. Look no good for what? What if I couldn't look good enough? So I whimpered some more and she went on worrying at me.

Sometimes, she slowed down as she passed my cot and said, 'Hello there.' Sometimes I smiled back. But if I smiled too much, she stopped and made me sit up, or even lifted me out and tried to make me stand. Then I was afraid of losing myself. As long as I stayed within the bars, I was safe.

'Look! I've found an ID card in the office. It might even be his. It doesn't match any of the others. Anyway, he can jolly well have it, then he can go too. It says he came from somewhere near Mi Hung.'

'D'you know the place? There might be some family still there who'd take him?'

'No, it's one of those resettlement areas inside the Iron Triangle. The village isn't there any more.'

'And the people?'

'Refugee camp. Closed down six months ago.'

'*Nguyen Thanh Ha*. Are you sure it's his?'

'Why not? Does it really matter? I mean, so long as he has a genuine card, that's all that counts. Then we can set about the emigration papers. *Nguyen Thanh Ha*. Sounds OK.'

How did you get here? I wanted to know but you didn't remember. You couldn't tell me. So I had to ask Patti.

'How did he get here? Who brought him out of the war?'

'He came on a plane. An airlift, it was called. A mercy flight. Mercy! I don't think anybody really believed there was any mercy involved. It was more some kind of publicity stunt for a newspaper.'

'Why did they do it?'

'Every day, cargo planes flew into the city bringing in supplies for the troops. Films, drink, newspapers, hamburgers, coke, soap. As well as the bombs and armaments. The planes flew out empty. Soap, drinks, films, bombs, all used up. Then somebody had a bright idea of shipping something *out* on those planes. One of the empty planes taking orphans to the US developed engine trouble. It came down in swampy land just after take-off. All the babies in it were killed instantly.'

'So if they were all killed, how did Ha get here?'

'That first crash didn't stop people thinking it was a good idea. Soon other groups all over the world were airlifting children out. They thought they were saving them. People in the Western world sponsored their tickets.'

'Did you sponsor Ha?'

'No. We sponsored a little girl called Phuong, a baby. She was in a makeshift orphanage somewhere in the city. We wanted to adopt her but we never did. I don't know what became of her.'

'But why Ha? Why him?'

'He came on a mercy flight too. But he was so damaged on arrival, they thought he wasn't fit for adoption. They didn't think it would work.'

'They were right. It isn't working, is it? It's awful. None of us will survive. He's destroying us all.'

'So instead of adopting him, we started sponsoring him, paying for his keep. We began soon after he'd arrived and every month ever since. So you see, in a way he's been your brother for several years. Since long before you knew him.'

'I've always known him.'

So that was how you were sent away from the orphanage in the war. On a mercy airlift. But you didn't know what mercy was. And when they were ready to send you away, a round-eyed woman in long, flowing robes came to your room.

'It's Sister Thérèse,' you heard one of the helpers say. 'From St Thomas's.'

'What's she want here? Hasn't she got enough to do back at her own place?'

'She wants to baptize them.'

'As *Christians*? How curious. Whatever for? They're mostly Buddhists and Confucians.'

'In case they die.'

The woman in the robes called Sister Thérèse stood at the end of your room.

'The first of the seven sacraments is Baptism, by which we are made Christians, children of God, members of His Holy Church, and heirs of Heaven.' She spoke in a loud, singing voice.

'If she cares about children dying, I'd have thought it'd be more relevant to clean out the drains back at her own orphanage, instead of fretting about baptizing our children. What's she going to do now? Put lace christening robes on them all?'

'Didn't you hear? One of the airlifts crashed on take-off. Galaxy. All the babies were killed. I saw them coming off in body bags. No one was baptized. That really upset her.'

The woman called Sister Thérèse came to each cot with a cup of water. She touched your head with the water and made a pattern on your forehead with her fingertips. She baptized you with the name Anthony, her brother's name. She hadn't seen him for five years.

So now your name is Anthony. She bent over and touched your cheek with her lips. You liked her face, her singing voice, the touch of her hand. You wanted her to stay with you. But she moved to the next cot to baptize the baby in the cot called Phuong, with the name Ursula.

'Queen of Heaven, rejoice! Alleluia!'

And when she had baptized everybody, she chanted a song about a mother. Somebody's mother.

'Holy virgin of virgins. Mother of Christ. Mother of divine grace. Mother most pure.'

What was a mother?

'Mother inviolate. Mother undefiled.'

Have I a mother?

'Mother most admirable. Mother of good counsel. Have mercy on us. Pray for us.'

I remembered a mother. An old woman with stained red teeth who spat red spittle. My mother's mother.

I remembered my mother. With memory came knowledge. With knowledge came pain.

'Mother of our Creator. Pray for us.'

I will not think about what I have lost. I will swing my head from one side to the other until I can't hear the woman speaking. Until I am asleep.

I rocked. I dozed. I woke and she still was there, still chanting her song.

'Queen of Angels. Queen of Martyrs. Queen of Peace. Lamb of God, you take away the sins of the world. Spare us.'

190

The people in the city believed there would be a bloodbath, that orphans and defectives would be murdered in their beds. They wanted peace with honour, quickly. It ended as another kind of peace.

You were prepared hurriedly for flight, but nobody explained what was happening to you. They took your photograph and they pinned a brown label to you. On to it, they copied the name, and the age which was printed on the ID card they had decided would be yours. Then you were picked from your cot and rushed from the room, along a corridor, down the stone steps, across the dusty courtyard, through the iron gates, and out to a waiting bus.

> It was the first time I'd left the room since I began, the first time since my life started. The sky outside seemed too bright. There was too much noise. I didn't know what was happening. I was afraid and I screamed. Another child screamed with me.

'It's all right, dear. Don't worry. It'll be nice. We're going in a lovely big plane. Don't be afraid. I'll take care of you.'

Those who could sit were placed upright on benches in the bus. Those who couldn't sit were laid on the floor on blankets. Each child had its brown tag flapping round its neck as the bus bumped along the pot-holed road.

The bus stopped on the edge of the airstrip at Tan Son Nhut. You were lifted out and heat surged up from the sticky, black tarmac, and hot air eddied round from the roaring engines. The rich fumes of diesel, the sweet, intoxicating smells of war. One adult carried each child, and they ran in single file, across the open tarmac, to where the great plane was standing to receive you, with its open mouth. The brown cards flapped in the hot wind. Long ago, you'd seen boys and men with brown labels flapping around their necks, and their arms secured behind their backs with twine, running towards such a gangway and up into such a dark opening. They were taken away and you never saw them return.

> I was held up to the window.
> 'Look, dear! Look, see we're taking off now. Bit of a jolt. Up we go. Flying in the air. Isn't it exciting! See the little houses down there.'
> There were puffs of smoke in the air around us. One

woman screamed that we were receiving incoming fire.

'Hail, Mary, full of grace.'

'The cheats! They promised they wouldn't interfere with the evacuation.'

'Not theirs. I think it's ours.'

I saw the land falling away. Trees, water green and white, all shrinking. I wanted to scream, to bite, to claw my way out through the window, to get down there before it was too late. My place was by the bright, shining water and the green fields. A thatched home with two rooms and space for a cow, and a hen-coop, and bright sunlight gleaming off the paddies. And green dappled shadows over the graves of the ancestors. I could see her face quite clearly now.

Inside the compartment it was dim, and the roaring blocked out all sounds. The stranger who was holding me spoke to me, but I heard no sound. I only saw the big, dark opening of her mouth forming senseless word shapes.

Below us buffaloes wallowed in water. Below us, I had once left a cow, tethered in a shelter. When I went, who took her out and fed her? Who milked her? Her udder would be tender and bloated with milk if nobody went to her, and she would be lowing in pain. But by now there was nothing I could do.

I turned away from the window. I'd remembered it all when it was too late.

I scratched at my head, and tugged at my hair till it hurt, to make pain so that I would remember where I used to live and who I lived with. I rocked my whole body from side to side. I must remember.

'It's his ear, I think. Probably the air pressure in here. Try and get him to swallow.'

Let me go back. I've remembered.

'Look, he's crying real tears! I wonder if he knows what's going on?'

PART FOUR

Brothers

Zigzag lights before my eyes, and rocking, and loud noises, and I saw myself carried in through the door into the nursery of The Chestnuts.

'Look, we're home. This is your home, Ha. Everything's going to be all right.'

'Don't keep calling him that ugly name. His name is Robert now. And that other child, the one they called Pham Thi Loan, she's to be Jane.'

'But do you think it's right to change their names? That's the only thing they've got left that's really their own.'

'How can they join in English playgroups with such silly names? Of *course* they must be changed.'

They took you to a children's home, Ha, called The Chestnuts. In England. This is England, here, a green and pleasant land. But it's a different kind of green from the one you're used to. It's a cooler, softer green and it's only here half the year, in spring and summer. And a children's home is a sort of place where children can live who haven't got any parents. Like you hadn't. That's where you went. You stayed there for years, till Patti came for you.

Food. Every day. Several times a day. There was food. It was on flat plates, set out round a wooden table. We didn't stay in our cots. They made us sit up at a table to eat the food. A plate was put before me and I was fed the food on it. I wanted it. I screamed for the food that was on the plate, on the table, out of reach of my mouth. So they fed it to me.

'Goodness knows who pays the fuel bills here! I'm glad it's not me.'

'Why do they keep it so hot all the time?'

'Because of the paralysed children. Otherwise they seem to get respiratory problems.'

So hot? It seemed to you so cold. Maybe because the colours were cold. Pale blue and grey. Cold colours. And dim bulbs hanging centrally from the ceilings. Cold, dim lights.

And cold, every day.

I had never felt like this before. They put more clothes on me. They pulled more garments up my legs. They pulled tight, woollen garments, which scratched my neck and which dragged at my ears, down over my head. Tight, bright clothes so I could hardly breathe. But I was warmer.

Food. Clothes. And now toys.

Clothed in layers of garments on my legs, on my chest, on my body, layers of sleeves covering my arms, they sat me on the cold, shiny floor with toys, and made us play. If we dozed off, they woke us.

'Come along, Robert. Not beddy-byes time now. Wake up. Look, we're going to do the jigsaw. See the pieces. Take the piece. Hold it in your hand, there. Good boy.'

I held the piece.

'No, don't eat it. No, put it down with the other piece, to make the nice picture. Can you see the picture we're making?'

Questions. Too many questions. Can you see? When did you last see?

Have you ever seen the enemy?

Why did you go out in the night?

Was there a loud noise?

Why do you pay taxes?

I didn't like the toys. I didn't like the clothes, and I didn't like the cold. But I liked the food. I was going to eat and eat. That was all I would do. Eating would be living. The food never stopped coming, three times a day, it came set out in plates around the edge of the low table, and we were lifted on to the chairs. The food was soft. Sometimes it was soft and savoury. Sometimes it was soft and sweet. Sometimes soft and warm. Occasionally soft and cold. It was pretty colours. The food was yellow, brown, red, green. It was never blue. The walls of the room where we sat were blue.

'Robert's a funny one, isn't he? He just eats and eats, and never seems to grow. Either upwards or outwards. Never gets fatter. I hope he'll get some teeth soon.'

'It really is time he learned to feed himself. A great boy like that, sitting there on a nursery chair with the toddlers, being fed. I'm sure he *could* feed himself if only he was shown how.'

So one of them took a spoon and taught me, but it was too slow. The coloured, soft food didn't reach my mouth fast enough.

'Come on, Robert, you're just being difficult. I'm sure you are. There's a good lad. I bet you could do it. No, you must learn. I'm not going to keep feeding you. I won't always be here, and the other girls won't want to keep doing it.'

'Ha! Wake up! Time to wake up! You can't fall asleep on the table!'

She lifted up my head. I had fallen into the softness.

Soft, sweet and warm.

'Oh Lord, look at him! He put his head in the bowl, all in the custard. It's revolting. I'm sure he did it on purpose.'

She held my head and wiped it with a cloth. I bit her.

After I had eaten several times a day, I could sleep. Always sleep, for as long as I could. Eating was good, and it helped me sleep.

I sat on the hard, shiny floor with the pieces of toys and I rocked my body from side to side, swing, swing. Movement led to escape.

Sometimes, when I rocked my body from side to side, I screamed, and as I turned from side to side, the scream sounded different, into one ear and away from the other, like noises going away and coming back. I liked to scream. It reminded me of sensations, of fear, of noise. My screaming reminded me of things which I could never quite catch. But if I screamed and rocked for long enough, I began to remember. I couldn't see what it was, but it was there, and I knew that I didn't want to remember after all. I heard exploding air in my ears and I felt confusion and loss.

I yelled loudly to drown the noise and fear. I merely moved from one terror to another. The only release was when I was eating.

The people there didn't like the screaming. Some slapped me. Some cradled me in their arms and sang to me. Some sat me outside in the dark passage away from the other children. Some lifted me up the stairs and laid me in my bed. Some gave me more food so that I was not able to scream.

When I stopped screaming, they brought me in from the dark passage, or down from my bed, or they cuddled me some more and told me I was good and could have a story.

She took me on her lap and opened a book with coloured pictures. She held up the book so that I could see and she pointed to the pictures. They were bright and shiny.

A picture of something to eat.

'Apple, dear. That's an apple, isn't it?'

A picture of something to put food in, a container for carrying rice.

'Basket. Shopping basket. Can you see the shopping basket, just like Matron has?'

A picture of an animal which scratches, and has its food in a dish on the floor.

'Cat. Pussy cat. We've got a cat here, haven't we?'

The animal's dish was in a corner of the room where they cooked. They put mounds of pink food in its dish. I slid along the hard, shiny floor on my bottom, to the corner, and ate the animal's food. But the creature came and scratched my face.

She showed me pictures of more food, and of machines, and of animals, and then came to a picture of a great aeroplane in a grey sky.

'Jet,' she said. 'An aeroplane. We call that one a jet. J for jet. J-E-T it says. Can you see it there in the picture? It flies high in the sky with lots of people in it, taking them on a holiday to the sunshine. You've been on a jet haven't you? You came all the way here on a big jet. Not many boys have been half-way round the world in a big jet. Aren't you lucky?'

The jet on the page leapt towards us through the sky, raining noise and darkness on to us, screaming with speed, red lights twinkling on its underside, screaming machine noise into our ears. I snatched at the book.

'No!' I cried, and tore at the page in her book.

'What on earth's the matter, dear? It's all right, calm now, dear.'

'No. No. No. No!' I screamed.

Then she began to scream too. 'Jean, did you hear? He

spoke! He said something. He said, "No".' She hugged me. 'You clever boy, Ha. That's right. No, you said it. Did you hear him? He really spoke. A real word. When we got to that picture of the plane. There's something about the picture he didn't like.'

'Let me take the book. I'll put it away for a while.'

'Ha, stop screaming now. It's all right.'

'Better give him a biscuit. That usually calms him.'

Some nights, men still came and spoke to you after everybody else in the children's home was sleeping. When they asked questions you were frightened that you might give the wrong answer. But at the same time, you welcomed their presence because they came from another time, when you lived in a different place. You could not recall that place, yet you knew that the soldiers had once been in that place too.

'Have you ever seen the enemy?' they asked you.

You did not know who the enemy was. You did not know if you had seen it or not.

'Yes,' you said. 'Sometimes.'

'Where did you see them?'

'I don't remember.'

'You remembered yesterday. Yesterday you told us where you saw them.'

'Yes. I was taken into the forest to help build tunnels.'

'Tunnels? What tunnels?'

'Where my father lived. The men had their food there, and their weapons, and hollows in the soil where they could sleep.'

'Did you want to build tunnels?'

'Yes.'

'Did you ever go into the tunnels?'

'Yes, when I was digging with the other children.'

'Weren't you afraid?'

'No.'

'Wasn't it dark?'

'I didn't mind the dark. I was only afraid of the worms.'

'What worms?'

'In the soil walls. There are worms, very small, like mites, that burrow into your skin when you lie on the earth all night. I didn't like that.'

'Will you show us these tunnels you helped build?'

'No, I don't know where they are.'

'Why don't you know?'

'We were blindfolded when we went out.'

'Why?'

Why? Why? Why? I don't know why. We just were.

'Weren't you afraid?'

'What of?'

'Of the blindfold?'

'No. It was my father tied it on. He was very gentle. The edge of the village was mined. He led us through very carefully. No one was ever hurt.'

'Who set the mines?'

'I don't know. Some other people. But they always said where the mines were with a special sign made with crossed sticks.'

A woman came and we were carried into the playroom where we had to play. One of the women sang songs, and told us stories.

The first story she told us was about a man who fell down from a wall and had an accident. Soldiers arrived to make him better but they could do nothing for him, so he remained, injured, on the ground.

It was a bad story. I didn't want to hear it. I didn't like stories about soldiers and wounded men. I don't think the other children did either, but Mrs Frinton thought it was a good story and made us sing it again and again.

'All right, if Robert doesn't want to join in, that doesn't matter. The rest of us will sing along without him. Humpty-Dumpty sat on a wall. Here we go now.'

I tried to tell Mrs Frinton about the stories I wanted to hear.

'Over five centuries ago, in the reign of King Tran Thuan Tong, a young mandarin named Tu Thuc went in search of the Land of Bliss. He sought a place of eternal spring, the air perfumed with the scent of lilies and roses, gold and silver fish swimming in the stream, broad lotus leaves floating gently on the surface of the sparkling waters.'

'And then, Goldilocks went upstairs in the three bears' house, and lay down on one of the beds.'

I wanted to hear about the peacocks who strutted across the lawns, and the princesses with stars in their hair. Mrs

Frinton told us about a great bear which chased a small girl out of his house and away through the forest.

'Over five centuries ago, in the reign of King Tran Thuan Tong, a young mandarin.'

But what came next?

'And so there he stayed for one hundred days.'

And then?

'The Fairy Queen was consulted.'

And what happened after that?

'She said, "If he wishes to return to the land of toil and sadness, to the land of brown dust, what is the point of keeping him here when his heart is still laden with earthly memories? His wish must be granted."'

And then?

But I could never remember how the story ended.

2

'Ha, somebody's coming to see you today. Somebody very special.'

You laughed, and crowed.

'Who d'you think it is?'

'Queen,' you said. 'Queen, queen, queen, queen.' You knew how they liked it if you said words.

'No, not the queen. Try again. Somebody who often comes to see you, and she sometimes brings you nice presents, and you have a nice time with her.'

'Santa,' you said. 'Santa, santa, santa, santa.' Santa was when you had lots of food all day, starting with oranges, chocolate, biscuits, and sweets which you found hanging at the end of your bed, pushed into your socks. You knew it was a special day when you found food had been put inside your clothes.

'No, it's not Santa. You know Santa Claus only comes down the chimney to see you once a year, at Christmas. He doesn't come all through the year. No, it's your friend coming. Your nice friend Patti. Coming to see you, coming to take you out for a treat.'

A treat? What was a treat? You had treats at the Festival of the Lanterns, and you had fireworks at the Festival of the Rice-planting. Do you remember the Festival of the Tombs, and the Feast of the Hungry Spirits? No, it's gone. Now you must have Santa and chocolate wrapped in your clothing.

They washed your face, combed your hair, and pulled a clean jersey on over your head.

'Come on, Ha, let's put on your shoes all ready.'

The shoes were heavy. You didn't like them.

'Now come along, dear. Be sensible. And walk properly. You know you can if you try. No, you don't need the walking-frame. Put it back. You can walk without. You want Patti to see you looking like a big boy, don't you?'

The friend called Patti came more often than Santa. But she didn't bring presents. She sat in the playroom and looked at picture-books with you. She sat at the play tables and did jigsaws. Sometimes, she talked to the other children, then you threw the jigsaw boxes on to the floor. Sometimes, she took you out in the wheelchair and pushed you round the garden. Once, she put you on the swing and pushed from behind. You didn't like it. You screamed and fell to the ground, so she didn't do it again.

You got to know her face. It never changed. The faces of the other people there often changed. They always did the same things. They washed you and dressed you and helped you downstairs. They put food for you. They looked at books with you. But their faces changed and they had no names.

The woman who visited you never changed, until one day she came in a blue coat instead of the brown one. You wouldn't look at her all afternoon.

'Ha, what is it? I'm your friend, Patti. You know me. I see you every week. Don't you want to talk to me today?'

Then, she came with a man and a car, and they took you in the car, travelling along the roads, and back again for more food.

She came again, and there was a boy in the car.

The boy came into the playroom with your friend Patti and you could see that he belonged with her. You looked at him when he wasn't looking at you. He didn't seem to know who you were, but you felt that you knew him already.

You didn't like the boy. He wasn't like you. He could do things which you couldn't do. He could walk and talk, and understand. He had memory and he had knowledge. And even when he had neither, he knew how to find out about all the things which you were most afraid of. You knew he would find out everything which you didn't want to remember.

The boy belonged with your friend Patti. Your friend Patti was his mother.

Everything which you wanted, he already had.

Even if you didn't like him you knew that you had to go with him in the car. They called him Simon and they said he was your brother. You had never had a brother, and you didn't want one now. But you had to go with him because he knew how to find out about all the things you feared.

Patti and Tony told you they were taking you home. You believed it and so you went with them in their car. You were bored with eternal youth in the Land of Bliss and you wanted to go back to your village. But when they got you home, it wasn't the home you expected. It was a long time since you'd been in your home. You had forgotten what it should be like. You just knew that this wasn't it. And the first night in the place they said was your home, you lay in a bunk-bed and dreamed yourself back to a place which was home. It was a cot in a long room. You knew *that* wasn't your real home either.

And the next night you dreamed you went home again. This time, you walked through a village, and found a home with two rooms which were clean and light and airy. With doors open on two sides to the sunlight. But you saw no people in the house, no livestock in the grassy yard. Nothing there. Just two empty rooms.

But gradually, week by week, you saw more. You saw the forest. You smelled the air scented with jasmine flowers. You saw the water-buffalo wallowing up to their necks in mud. But the things you most wanted to see were lost. The young woman, and the old woman, the young man, and the baby girl. Then, the things you didn't want at all, began to come. The images of noise, of fear, of darkness, of soldiers. And once they had come, they were always there. The boy Simon had made them come back because he had knowledge and memory.

'Come on all of you. Smile nicely. You too, Ha. Smile at the camera. Say cheese.'

'What d'you want pictures for, Patti? You know I hate having my photograph taken.'

'I want to send some to Granny. And Claire said she'd like one. And, well it's always nice to keep records. You're both growing so much. We might forget what you ever looked like if we haven't got some nice snaps in the album.'

So you and I stood side by side at the front door and let Patti take a roll of snaps of us. We were wearing our matching striped sweaters which Patti liked because she thought it made us look like brothers.

You'd seen photographs taken before. The men had cameras strung around their necks. They'd taken photographs of Giau Huc on the ground, and of the hut burning in the rubber plantation, and of a starving child in a cot. Thinking of those images filled you with a sense of loss because you could only remember the bad things. You couldn't remember the rest.

'Patti, haven't you taken enough now? I've got to go and do my homework, and Ha doesn't like standing here either. He's crying.'

Patti ran forward and put her arms round you. 'Ha, what is it, darling?' she said. 'Whatever's the matter?'

'He doesn't like having his photograph taken, that's all.'

It's OK, Ha. It doesn't matter if you can't remember everything yet. I'll try and remember for you. The good parts too, and I'll tell you.

I didn't really know many good parts. But I'd try.

Mostly, I wanted to believe that my mother, Ha's mother, the other mother we had, was still alive. I wanted to believe that she hadn't died. If Ha got out of the pit, perhaps she did too. I wanted to believe that she had feigned death and been able to get away.

'Tony,' I said. 'Just supposing Ha's real mother did trace him to here? What would you say?'

'If it was before the adoption was through, she'd have every legal right to claim him, of course.'

'And if the adoption had already been done, and then she turned up wanting him?'

'Since we're scheduled to go to court next month, it's really quite unlikely that some South-East Asian bar-girl —'

They still seemed to think she was a bar-girl. She only went to the wooden huts once because she had to have the money.

'She was a hard-working farmer,' I said.

'All right, Simon. Sorry. Nonetheless, a hard-working Asian peasant woman is unlikely to appear on our doorstep. But if she did, and if she could give proof that Ha was indeed her son, we would do everything we possibly could to help her and look after her.'

'And we'd make room for her here, wouldn't we? If she wanted to stay?'

3

Upstairs, Ha had an accident. He stood in the passage quite still, a mournful look on his face.

Wet and smelly. Both.

'You'd better go to the bathroom,' I said sharply. 'I'll fetch Patti for you.'

But he didn't dare move by himself, just stood there with his legs slightly apart, so I had to lead him along, and I stood him on the bath-mat so the mess wouldn't spread. 'You just wait here and I'll get her.'

I undid his shirt buttons and his shoe-laces so he could start undressing himself, then I ran downstairs. But Patti wasn't in the kitchen, although there was a half-made cucumber salad on the table and a kettle boiling.

I heard their voices outside, her and Tony's. They were to-gether at the far end of the back garden, sitting side by side in a patch of light where the sun just manages to squeeze past the walls of the house opposite. Patti's climbing rose was coming into bloom and the evening light was touching the petals of the flowers. On the ground at her feet stood a bottle of wine, in a mixing bowl of ice. They were sharing the same glass and giggling. They were so wrapped up in each other they didn't even see me.

The two things I hated most. Parents drinking at inappropriate times and parents excluding me.

It was a pink-coloured wine, and as Tony lifted up the glass, the sun glanced through it making it seem shot with pink ice. What were they doing giggling and drinking pink wine at tea-time?

Then I remembered the anniversary.

I wanted to run across and apologize. Sorry Patti, Tony. Quite forgot. The present I usually make, the card, the bunch of flowers I buy and the way they always kiss me and thank me so profusely.

But it wasn't *my* anniversary. It was theirs. Marriage. To each other. I hadn't been there at the wedding, so why was I always trying to edge in on the celebration?

But she must come in and clean Ha. He was her child. She had wanted him in the family. It was her duty to come and attend to him when he was soiled.

I listened to them. They hadn't laughed like that when we were a perfect Trinity. Before Ha. Had I always spoiled her girly giggles?

So I didn't call her. Even if I was excluded, I wasn't alone. I had Ha upstairs. Slightly soiled. If Patti and Tony belonged together, then so did Ha and me.

If I have ever done anything brave in my life, it was then, when I decided not to call Patti to come and see to her responsibilities. The bravest thing in my life. I left them to each other and went quietly back through the kitchen, turning off the kettle on my way, and taking a hunk of cheese and a slice of cucumber to fortify myself for the ordeal ahead.

He was still standing exactly where I'd left him, immobile in his mess. He hadn't even begun to try and undress.

'Sorrah, Shimoo,' he said. 'Sorrah.' As though he really meant it.

'That's OK, Ha,'

'I make messy yuk, yuk, yuk, yuk.'

Men do what he had done, when they are afraid. Even grown men. When they are about to go into battle, or when they are about to be hanged. But what was there for Ha to be afraid of now?

Don't be afraid. Not of being in this family. You're safe here.

But perhaps if a person has once been afraid, he goes on being afraid for a long time.

'Never mind. We all make mistakes sometimes.'

I put the plug in the bath and turned on the taps.

'What you do?'

'Filling the bath. What d'you think I'm doing? To wash you.'

'Yeah,' he said, as though he understood. 'Dis day, *you* washer me.' Not a question. A statement of fact. Perhaps he *does* understand some things?

I undressed him. It's a tricky job undressing a boy who's done what he'd done. Half-way through, I had to open the bathroom window to let out the pong. Yet all the time I felt an exhilaration with myself. I was doing something I'd never done before. Washing Ha after his accident in his pants was the second bravest thing I'd done.

I got the water right, not too hot, not too cold. I helped him into the bath and poured in a measure of antiseptic to be on the safe side. I washed him with soap, and rinsed him with clean water.

205

They had kept facts from me. I shall keep secrets from them. I shall keep good secrets. I shan't tell them I cleaned Ha up today. I shan't tell them what Ha and I talk about. They may think he's their adopted son. But he's something different to me, which is more important and more lasting.

'Dis day, you do it,' said Ha.

'Yes,' I said. 'It's Mum and Dad's anniversary. They're busy having a chat and a good time together. I'm bathing you now.'

'Why you washer me?'

'Because I'm your brother.'

'Yeah. Brudding. You me brudding. Yeah, yeah, yeah, yeah.'

I expect I'll grow quite fond of him always saying things four times over.

'And brothers look after each other. Once you're a brother, you stay a brother for always. All right?'

'Yeah, yeah, yeah!' Only three yeahs just when I was getting used to four.

'Can you say that? Brother? I am your brother? And tell me what it means.'

'Always. Long time. Brother friend.'

'Yes, quite right.'

I dried him, and put talcum powder on him. I helped him dress in clean clothes, and I managed to hug him very quickly.

Then we went downstairs. The parents were still mooning in the evening light.

'We'll go out, Ha, down to the chippie and get some chips to keep us going.'

Ha tugged at his push-chair standing in the hall.

'No, Ha. Not the buggy today.'

He pulled it again. 'Yeah, yeah. Can't walk.'

'Rubbish. I've seen you. If you want to come out with me, you come on foot. Like a boy.'

He shrugged and came.

Half-way down the high street, he reached for my hand.

'No, you don't hold my hand.'

'Why? Why can't not? Ha like you.'

'Yes, I know you like me. But even if you do like me, you can't hold my hand because, well, because brothers just *don't*.'

But how did I know? I'd never had a brother before. 'I mean, Ha, I've never *seen* brothers holding hands, not when they're as old as us.'

So instead, he linked his arm in mine and we walked along to the chippie arm in arm, Ha stumbling on his weak, ricketty legs.

We ate our chips from the packet, slowly, walking home. And then, on the way back down the high street, we met three big louts with short, cropped hair and laced DMs, from Rosehill Estate.

'Give us a chip, guv'nor,' one called out.

Another whistled at us, an insinuating, sexy whistle because we were so close and arm in arm.

'Here comes Mr Chinky Chinaman.'

They moved in, and walked on either side of us. Ha clung more firmly to my arm, but he smiled, and with him beside me, I found I wasn't afraid. And when I wasn't afraid, they didn't hit me or throw stones. They merely jostled us a bit from side to side across the pavement. Ha even seemed to like it.

'He with you, is he?' one asked me.

I nodded.

'Seen him about. Goes up the loony school, don't he?'

'Yes.'

'What's his name?'

'Ha.'

'Ha? Ha ha ha. Good name for someone like him!'

Ha, recognizing his name, laughed and then they all laughed.

'He's one of them loonies, isn't he?'

'Not exactly,' I said. 'He was born in a war.'

'Oh yeah?' the boy nearest me jostled us some more. 'Tell us another. He don't look old enough to me! My grandar were in a war. He's going on seventy!'

One of the others laughed. 'I seen your grandar an all! You thought he were like that because he's old. Now you know! He's like that because he were in a war.'

They all fell about laughing. Ha laughed too. I wanted to stop him because he didn't understand why he was laughing.

'Which war was our young friend in, then?' one of the boys asked.

'Just an ordinary war, like any other. There've been lots of wars.'

'Got shot up, did he?'

'Yes,' I said.

'Under heavy fire? Boy soldier?'

'No. Not a soldier. Just a casualty of war.'

'That what it do to you, being shot up? If you get caught up in a war? Make you kind of strange like that?'

207

'It depends,' I said. 'It does sometimes.'

They all three seemed impressed.

'Well, be seeing you guv'nor. Ta, rar.'

The parents had finished gooing at each other and were preparing supper together, in a soppy, slow, loving manner.

'Anniversary supper, darlings!' Patti called to me as she heard us come in. 'Salmon, cucumber salad, mayonnaise, and strawberries. All right?'

'Good,' I called back.

'Be a little while yet,' she called again. 'Hope you're not starving.'

'No, we're fine,' I said. I followed Ha upstairs.

He squatted down in our room, tipped his toy-box up all over the floor and began to pick out some Lego bricks.

'What can I do for you, Ha?' I said.

'Gimme Lego,' he said and grinned. 'Want all Lego, all lotta Lego. Want all toys. Lotta toy. Gimme all.'

He was surrounded already by all the Lego there was in the house, including the Lego Aunt Claire had given him, and several pieces he'd pinched from the school, as well as the Lego out of the attic which I'd had when I was younger.

I put on the cans and slotted in my Vivaldi. Ha, in his inept and cumbersome way, began to build a little vehicle out of Lego. In my childhood I used to make buses, and schools, homes, shops and quiet country railway stations. Ha now used the same bright, primary coloured pieces, the red, yellow, blue, and white blocks, the green rectangular base bricks, and I saw clearly what he was making, just as he saw it, for we were two brothers.

Ha was making an M-42 tank, with seven wheels and caterpillar tracks on each side, with three men mounted on top, and one inside the turret, with two long, waving radio aerials. I watched Ha take up a handful of pretty blue Lego bricks and snap them into place so that each man now wore a flak jacket and a criss-cross bandolier of ammunition. Another cube of coloured Lego and each was armed with an M-16 rifle and a grenade launcher.

'Soldier car! Look, Shimoo! Look soldier car got wheel, got gun, got more, more, more, more gun most.'

The M-42 moved into position overlooking Route 1 in Quang Ngai province.

'Actually, Ha,' I said, taking off the cans. 'I suppose I meant it rhetorically, if you know what that means. It means, of course I'll give you my Lego, all my possessions. But that's only a beginning. What can I do for you after that?'

He wasn't really listening because down through the sky came a B-52 with thirty tons of deadly cargo, swooping towards the Lego village under the legs of the bunkbed. A 340 kg bomb hit the patterned rug on the floor, and then another. One red plastic figure toppled and with him, 100,000 men from the North were killed. One blue plastic figure fell and with him 400,000 men from the South were killed.

'I mean, Ha, how could I help you for the future? You've lived and I've only been dreaming all my life. In a way, I envy you because you've lived and endured and suffered, and I've just been here. Can you believe that I actually envy you? So what's the best thing to help us both?'

An M-113 armoured personnel carrier moved bumpily over the woollen tufts of the rug, its passengers leaping out to combat an enemy target, to shatter and flatten the whole of Legoland, to deactivate all gun emplacements, to search and to destroy.

When the raid was over, Ha sent in the Lego ambulance to make it all be better, swept the Lego pieces back into the toy box and turned his cherubic face to me.

'Story, Shimoo. Storytime.'

I fetched a book from the shelf.

'Not bear.' He meant, not Goldilocks and the three bears.

'I thought you *liked* that one? About the big bear who says, don't you come into *my* house?'

'Not bear. Tell me story me. Story about me, and killing and soldier go bang. Dey get dead, me not dead big bomb crash.'

'I don't know that sort of story. It sounds horrible.'

He took hold of my face in his hands and looked directly into my eyes.

'Yes, yes, yes, yes. Do,' he said, and he knew that I knew which story he wanted.

So I told it every night. Each evening I climbed into the lower bunk with him and he snuggled up close under my arm and I told him a little part of the story he wanted. Sometimes he remembered things which I didn't remember, and as he learned to speak better he added them in.

'Can you remember the village yet, Ha? Just a bit?'

'Smashed,' he said. 'Smash, smash, smash. All gone dead.'

'I know that's how it *was*, but nothing's ever completely dead. You might not recognize it as it used to be, but it's still there.'

'Not go back. Too far.'

'We can't go back properly because you belong here with me. But we can think about it together.'

So we walked back through the village together in our minds and I held his hand tight so he wouldn't be afraid. We saw that the village was deserted, the huts long since gone, but we also saw the flattened ground softened with new bamboos springing up. The red river still flowed, and where the vegetable plots had once been, a small patch of earth was freshly tilled, and planted with two rows of maize.

When I told us his story a second time, I recorded it on to my tapes. It meant having to scrub out Vivaldi, but at least it means we now have the story together on nine cassettes which we keep in the bottom drawer of our chest, so that it's always there whenever we want to remember what it was like being a child in a war. We used to listen a lot, though we don't need to so much now.

One day, we'll go back to his country for real. I'm going to become a botanist, specializing in the tree-ferns of South-East Asia. That way, my fare will be paid. Ha will always be my assistant.

We'll try and look for Ha's other mother while we're there.

'Won't we, Ha?'

'Yeah.'

Patti and Tony think it's unlikely she's still alive. But if Ha survived perhaps she did too. And when we do find her, she will have to accept us as her sons because we belong together now.

Author's Note

Most of the things which happen in this story are based on true
events, though they did not necessarily happen to one person. If
you are interested to know more about what happens to
ordinary people when there is a war, *The Village of Ben Suc* by
Jonathan Schell (Cape, 1967) is about a resettlement camp like
the one in this story, and *Dust of Life* by Liz Thomas (Hamish
Hamilton 1977. Paperback: Collins, Fount, 1978) tells about a
girl who went to work with some of the parentless children on
the streets of Saigon.

In 1975, at the end of the Vietnam war, there were said to be
800,000 abandoned children in the city of Saigon. Wars always
create orphans. By now, there are other wars, and other orphans.

THE WHITE NIGHTS OF ST. PETERSBURG

Geoffrey Trease   ISBN 0 86267 196 5

To David, arriving from America to spend a year learning Russian and assessing the business prospects for his industrialist father who had hopes of Russo-American co-operation, St. Petersburg in the autumn of 1916 was a baffling though not unfriendly city. There were disquieting undertones, odd occurrences, and always the war in the background, but David often found it hard to believe everything his student friend, Anton, told him. Before David's year was out he found himself witness to a cataclysmic event: the Russian Revolution.

Geoffrey Trease writes of the city now called Leningrad with first-hand knowledge of its exquisite river vistas and graceful buildings. He has re-created its famous 'white nights' when the sun scarcely dips below the horizon.

THE LAST HARPER

Julian Atterton   ISBN 0 86267 184 1

This novel by Julian Atterton was shortlisted for the Young Observer Teenage Fiction Prize. Set in sixth-century Britain it tells how Gwion is forced to leave his home settlement after it is raided by sea wolves and how he finally becomes apprenticed to a master harper in the Kingdom of Rheged.

Julian Atterton is a young writer of great promise. He lives with his wife in a remote house on the North Yorkshire Moors and spends his time writing and researching into medieval history. He has studied at the Sorbonne in Paris and at the Universities of Cambridge and East Anglia. His interests include rock climbing, archaeology and acting.

THE YEAR OF THE STRANGER

Allan Campbell McLean   ISBN 0 86267 199 X

The stranger came to Skye that terrible year of 1877. It was the year that Mata the tinker had died a brutal death for salmon poaching and the time, too, that a blight had fallen on the crofting village so that it seemed forever cursed. And Calum Og had been beaten senseless by his uncle, but had gained his liberty.

'Allan Campbell McLean takes as his canvas the hard, austere life led by fishermen on the Isle of Skye a century ago, and he merges with it a fascinating tale of fantasy ... Mr McLean's skill at blending fantasy with fact is at its best.'

The Times Educational Supplement

THE SENTINELS

Peter Carter   ISBN 0 86267 195 7

When John Spencer's parents die his uncle packs John off into the Royal Navy as a 'Gentleman Volunteer'. His ship, HMS Sentinel is bound for the worst service in the Navy, the West African Squadron, the anti-slavery patrol.

Torn by civil war and shattered by the impact of fire-power, the tribal organisation of West Africa is breaking down. One man taken as a slave is Lyapo, a farmer, captured by Dahomey warriors. Chained, desperate, separated from his wife and children, Lyapo is passed from trader to trader until he is bought by the ruthless American, Kimber, master of the slave-ship Phantom. Bound for the plantations of America, Lyapo now faces the hazards of the high seas where, when Sentinel and Phantom meet, he finds himself joining John Spencer in a desperate struggle for survival.

Winner of The Guardian Children's Fiction Award 1981.

ROBINSHEUGH

Eileen Dunlop   ISBN 0 86267 194 9

Robinsheugh stands in the Scottish Border Country, a region where the line between the past and the present seems curiously indefinite. Elizabeth Martin is sent there to spend a summer with an aunt who seems more concerned with Robinsheugh's eighteenth-century owners that with her own niece, though a few years back the two of them had enjoyed a warm friendship. To Elizabeth, desperately lonely, unsure of herself and of others, the old house itself offers a strange alternative to misery — but one for which a harsh price has to be paid.

'It is dominated by the theme of the historical imagination and its power under certain circumstances to eclipse the present entirely . . . an impressive first book.'

The Times Literary Supplement

A FLUTE IN MAYFERRY STREET

Eileen Dunlop   ISBN 0 86267 183 3

Edinburgh's new Town is the city's beautiful late eighteenth-century quarter, and a tall quiet but somewhat sad house in one of its shabbier streets is the setting for this second novel by Eileen Dunlop. Here live three members of the once prosperous Ramsay family, and when we first meet them, none of them is very content with daily life. Mrs Ramsay wonders how she can make ends meet. Marion feels her existence appallingly restricted by ill-health, and Colin pines for something he can never, he thinks, have — a flute of his own.

Award winning author, Eileen Dunlop was born at Alloa, and educated in Alloa and Edinburgh. She has worked with children all her life and is currently Head of the Preparatory School of Dollar Academy. Her novels which have won high acclaim include *Robinsheugh (Swallow)*, *Fox Farm*, *The Maze Stone*, *Clementina*, and *The House on the Hill*.

NO HERO FOR THE KAISER

Rudolf Frank   ISBN 0 86267 200 7

The world closed in on Jan Kubitzky on September 1914 — his fourteenth birthday. Russian soldiers, armed with guns and cannon were in the fields and similarly armed German soldiers were in the wood. Between them lay the small Polish hamlet of Kopchovka, which had been Jan's home until the day when everything in it was destroyed. When the firing stopped, only he and Flox, Vladimir the shepherd's dog, were left alive.

'*NO HERO FOR THE KAISER* is a work so remarkable that you have to wonder why it has taken so long to reach us here. The German-born author served in the 1914 war, and wrote the book from that experience. It was banned and publicly burned by Hitler in 1933. Its acclaim, we learn continues . . . Graphic, memorable . . . it's clear to see why this book was put to the flames.'

Naomi Lewis *The Observer* 1986